with the Season's Greetings
and all good wishes
Christmas 1933

FROM A COTTAGE IN
PENNYCOOK LANE

FROM A COTTAGE IN PENNYCOOK LANE

By
ISABEL CAMERON

Illustrated by
SAVILE LUMLEY

LONDON
THE RELIGIOUS TRACT SOCIETY
4 BOUVERIE STREET, E.C.4

First published in 1933
(All Rights Reserved)

.

Made in Great Britain

CONTENTS

ILLUSTRATIONS

ILLUSTRATIONS

ILLUSTRATIONS

EXPLAINING MRS. MACKAY

THE spring of 1924 was long and cold; influenza raged, depression ruled. Yet I look back on the time with pleasure, for a friend said: "Go and see Aunt Jane and listen to her homely fireside chats. They'll do you more good than a trip to the sunny South."

Somewhat diffidently (for I did not know the lady) I obeyed. I found her a never-ending source of help and cheer. One simply couldn't continue in the "blues" whilst in her company. Her philosophy was sound and was seasoned with pawky humour.

Once she said, "I'd like fine that when I passed along the Lane for the last time, my neighbours peeping at my funeral from behind their blinds would say:

' Poor old Jane is away! Well, she had her faults like the rest of us, *but she was aye cheery.*' "

A homely ambition? Perhaps. A glowing fire on the hearth is a homely thing but it draws us like a magnet. And because we warm our chilled hands at it, we go forth to the world once more feeling greatly helped and cheered. So is it with all who have warmed their cold hands at the cheery spirit of my friend.

When first I knew her, the household consisted of John her " goodman " and of her two sons, Jack and Robbie. One wet evening Jack took home, with numerous apologies, a small bundle of wet fur calling itself a puppy and a terrier at that. All it needed was shelter for a day or two till a more suitable home could be found. Jack suggested in faltering tones that perhaps they'd better drown it. . . . It is unnecessary to state that " Tooks " is easily the most cherished and pampered member of the home. And I'd just like to see the reception given to anyone offering him another!

Everyone in the village has a warm corner in their heart for "Aunt Jane " as we affectionately call Mrs. Mackay. Her loyal old neighbours, Mrs. Allen and Mrs. Keith, became in time my friends too, and to meet Captain Breezy and his wife was a sheer joy; an experience the remembrance of which kept one chuckling for days afterwards.

Aunt Jane was full of inconsistencies. To quote a

proverb to her or to suggest giving her a fountain pen filled her with fury. She had a firm conviction that John made a point of helping himself to her match-box; she was always hiding it in such secure places that she herself could not find it again.

She was not—oh most decidedly not—"A creature far too bright or good for human nature's daily food." But we liked her fine! She was so human. In the following pages she speaks for herself.

ISABEL CAMERON

FEAR AND FAITH

I HAVE many a time been greatly helped by the message
of the "Wayside Pulpit" fastened to the outside of
our church. I wonder who first thought of this way of
bringing a message of cheer to hurried, worried,
working folks, often so pressed for time that they have
little to spare for anything but the daily round and the
common task.

This particular morning I was troubled very much
about something that had happened to John. The
foreman of the engine room where John makes his
rivets and boilers told him that the firm was sending a
young man, Harry Bruce, to work along with him to
get some insight into the new machinery lately
installed.

The thought that had sprung up in both our minds
when we heard this news was that when the newcomer
had learned "the trick of the tools" John was to be
sacked. They'd say he was too old, that he should rest,

17

and so on. But he'd be *sacked*. Is there, in all our language, a sadder or a more terrifying word?

" Give us each day our daily *task*," is a prayer often on our lips and in our hearts during these days of unemployment. I must confess my heart was full of dread and fear as I went along to the butcher's for a pound of shin of beef, which, if you cook it long enough in a casserole, can taste as good as rump steak.

John would have a good dinner when he came home! Let no one despise a good meal when they are worried. We say, and believe it too, that we can't eat a bite, but when a tasty, well-cooked meal is set in front of us, it's wonderful what we can do. And the help it gives us is wonderful too.

It was then I caught a glimpse of the message on the " Wayside Pulpit." It was: " When Fear knocked at the door—Faith opened—and there was no one there." Twice I read it over, so as to get the full meaning, and then, like a waft of sweet briar after a shower of rain, came the sweet helpfulness of the message.

Fear, why, it dogs our steps from the cradle to the grave! After every deliverance we say: " Well, I won't fear again." But we do. We say, " God helped me yesterday, but I'm not at all sure He'll help me to-day."

My *Faith* is the most weak-kneed thing you ever saw. But the message comforted me greatly, and as I cooked

the dinner, putting in plenty of onions which John
loves, I pondered over the message. Supposing John
did lose his job, supposing Harry Bruce did get it—the
world wouldn't come to an end. Some other job might
turn up. If it didn't, John would be all the better for

" YOU'RE MRS. MACKAY, AREN'T YOU? "

a long rest. (Privately speaking, the thought of John
idle at home while other men went forth to their labour
made me feel sick.) But the blow hadn't fallen yet.

At this point there came a tap on the door. A young
and nice-looking woman was standing there. She had
a friendly face, but just at that moment she was looking
worried.

19

"You're Mrs. Mackay, aren't you?" she asked. "I'm Harry Bruce's wife, and my baby is ill. I sent to the workshop for Harry, you see I know no one yet, and I thought my baby was dying. Your husband, who is so kind to my husband, said he thought you would help me. Will you please? We're in lodgings in the meantime."

I put the casserole into a safe part of the oven and accompanied the poor worried young mother to her lodgings. She had got rooms with Mrs. Sim in the far-off end of Pennycook Lane. I haven't been reading nursing hints all these years without having some sort of an idea of what to do in an emergency when Baby has been eating things he had no business to eat.

Mrs. Bruce's baby, a poor, distressed little mortal, absorbed all our attention for the next hour, but when we got him comforted and the trouble in his tummy put right, he fell sound asleep. I advised the young mother to get in touch with our " angel in blue," the district nurse, who would help her and advise her about diets.

She said she would. " But," she added, " we're only to be here for a few weeks; just long enough for Harry to get to understand the new machinery. He told me your husband is so kind to him, and is showing him all the things he needs to know."

I was suddenly conscious of a lump in my throat, for

it couldn't have been easy for John to do this, especially when you remember he feared the younger man was to get his job. You may laugh if you like, but I never was so proud of my goodman in all my life as I was then.

Mrs. Bruce went on: " The firm's new branch in Boltley is opening soon and Harry will be in charge of the bolts and rivets. But he could never do this work if your husband hadn't been so kind."

The message of the " Wayside Pulpit " came into my mind like a shaft of sunshine on a gloomy day. Fear knocked—Faith opened—and *there was no one there*. The thing we had feared never happened!

. . . . . .

When John came home at dinner time we opened our hearts to each other. The same dread had been with both of us. He had learned only that morning that Harry Bruce was a temporary worker and that his own job was waiting for him as usual. He too had heard the knock of Fear at the door, and on going to open it in helping Harry Bruce—behold it fled. There was no one there! So is it ever with those fears and doubts of ours!

FLAGS OR UMBRELLAS

One day last year the King was expected to pass
through our part of the country. We were all tremen-
dously excited about it, of course; so were the " City
Fathers," and those in charge of our public affairs,
and men were sent out to see that the roads were all in
good order, that there was no " pot holes " on the way,
" and that every valley should be exalted, and every
mountain made plain," for the royal procession.

The schoolchildren were given a half-holiday, and
in charge of teachers they lined the roads on both
sides. The fly in the ointment was, as usual, the
weather! The sky was cloudy, and every now and then
there was a sharp shower of rain, after which the sun
would shine forth gloriously. It was interesting to
watch how the crowd prepared for the weather. The
young folks, bless their optimistic hearts, were all
armed with flags, but the older ones, sensible and dull,

had umbrellas! I suppose the ideal thing would have been to carry both an umbrella and a flag, but then none of us ever do behave ideally, do we?

And, after all, the flags had it! For just as the royal cars came in sight, the sun blazed forth handsomely and the flags made a gay rainbow of colour in the road. The children climbed up on garden walls, on the roofs of sheds, anywhere they could stand, and raised their flags. I'm quite sure the King was glad that flags, not umbrellas, carried the day!

No doubt, a flag won't keep you dry, as an umbrella will, but what umbrella ever raised your spirits to the skies, and filled your heart with wild gaiety as a flag does? A flag, a banner, why, the very names are full of romance and glamour. They have a history behind them that takes us back to the very dawn of civilization. I defy anyone to get sentimental about an umbrella!

It is for us to decide what we are to carry with us from day to day in order to meet the storm and stress of everyday life. The prudent ones will continue to carry umbrellas, which will keep them dry, but which will prevent them from seeing the glory of the sky and clouds. Why, the very word umbrella means something which shades one, and who wants to be shaded, I'd like to know? Besides, there's something awfully selfish about an umbrella! The person who holds it is protected, but the person who walks behind or before is liable to get his eye poked out, or a little trickle of rain drops down his neck, and the feelings thus aroused are anything but Christian. A selfish contraption is an umbrella.

But a flag now, tossing gaily in the wind, is never anything but an inspiration. We can recall old flags we have seen, flags tattered and torn, and stained, and how we glory in them, how proud we are of them, and when we see a man bearing a banner in front of his company of soldiers we envy him his position.

Yes, I'd fifty thousand times rather be a flag-bearer than an umbrella-bearer. One may get drenched with the rain, but what glory of sea and sky and cloud do we behold! One may prudently look after No. 1, but who's the better for that? Do the folks we meet and pass square their shoulders, and look bravely ahead, because they have met us with our selfish, prudent, dull umbrella?

Do you remember the old story we used to read in our history books of the landing of the Romans in this country? The Britons had all crowded to the edge of the water, and were looking threateningly at the approaching galleys. For a moment the Romans wavered, then one soldier seized the Roman standard, leaped overboard, and made his way to the shore. The others, inspired by the sight, followed, and so once more Cæsar " came, saw and conquered."

24

Had he carried an umbrella instead of the standard, I can see those other soldiers all fumbling in their baggage for their gamps, and " swithering " as to whether they should or should not follow the young

A MAN BEARING A BANNER IN FRONT
OF HIS COMPANY

leader. On the whole, I bet they'd decide to stay where they were, and presently they'd turn their galleys, and set sail again for Rome! Had this been the case, what would have become of us? We'd have none of the

Roman laws, and Roman roads, and Roman streets, which have been such blessings to our land!

I refuse to believe that Columbus's sailors would have followed him to American ground if he had planted an umbrella instead of the flag of his country and so claimed the new land for the old.

When we adventure out on the sea of life in search of new lands let us, especially the young ones, take a flag and carry it aloft. It will make us " more than conquerors," and it will inspire our fellow men and fellow women.

A CAT-AND-DOG LIFE

WHEN I open the outer door in the morning to take in the milk and the newspapers, Tooks always bounds out after me. He races into the middle of the road and challenges the whole world in general, and the next door cat in particular, to " come out and come on."

The cat next door is a large sleek animal called Lady Black. She has a haughty and insolent stare, and a stately way of looking straight over Tooks' head, which simply maddens him. She has a perfectly exasperating way of sitting on the top of the garden wall and gazing abstractedly into the distance, pretending that she does not know that an extremely angry little dog is yapping at the bottom of it!

" Come down, come down, and let me have a word with you," Tooks shrieks, dancing about in frenzy. She always declined the invitation till the other morning, when she surprised everybody, but especially Tooks, by accepting it. He was the most amazed dog in town.

" Yes? " she said, standing foursquare in front of him. " Did you want to speak to me? Here I am then."

Tooks *withered*. The bark died in his throat—his knees sagged beneath him and his tail fitted itself into the smallest possible compass.

" U-u-m," he mumbled. "Ah, excuse me. I think I see my friend Labby over there. I must have a word with him." As he scuttled past—would you believe it? —the cat next door cuffed him on the ear and he yelped. I blushed for him.

He was very unhappy about it himself, and his pretended gaiety and high spirits deceived no one. His conduct for quite a while after this puzzled me. Every afternoon he used to disappear. He is a friendly little fellow (except to cats and postmen) and everyone in the street knows and likes him, so I did not worry. But it used to surprise me with what a careless eye he looked upon his supper when he did return home.

I went to call on Mrs. Clark last Friday. She is the lady who owns the cat next door. She has been ill for a long time, and is just beginning to sit beside her bedroom fire. To my astonishment she told me that Tooks is in the habit of coming to her house every day to play with Lady Black and her kittens. He also joins them at supper.

"Just take a peep into the kitchen," she said, " and you'll see a sight that will amuse you."

I saw the sight—it did not amuse me; it filled me with dismay. On the hearth rug, stretched luxuriously

HIS EXPRESSION WAS AMIABLE—ALMOST
MAUDLIN IN FACT

at her ease, lay Lady Black. Three little balls of fluff that she calls kittens were playing about her, and sitting keeping watch and ward over the family was—Tooks! His expression was amiable—almost maudlin in fact. He was making queer little sounds in his throat, or perhaps in his stomach, which he imagined pleased the kittens. Lady Black languidly licked her family indiscriminately and, I give you my word, when Tooks reached over to play with the littlest kitten, Lady Black licked—his face! More, he seemed to like it!

Fascinated, I stood gazing at the scene. When a playful kitten climbed up Tooks' back and invited him to carry her to their saucer of food, Tooks obeyed. He giggled with delight! That dog had lost his manhood! Lady Black gazed insolently over her shoulder at him and then her green eyes caught sight of me and she sat up demurely. She said something to Tooks who was drinking milk out of the kittens' saucer with noisy enthusiasm, and then Tooks saw me!

" Tooks! " I said, in a voice charged with reproach and grief. He began a vigorous thumping with his tail upon the floor. He tried to appear as if he were quite at his ease. It was a deadly failure. The littlest kitten could see through him. I turned away, but I could see with the tail of my eye that Tooks had risen and was following me.

We went homeward in solemn silence. We are not speaking to each other since. *"Cats "* is no longer the master word to send Tooks flying into the road with a challenging bark.

John, who as usual sides with the evildoer, tickles his ears and calls him " good doggy."

But life is for all of us a clouded affair. The only one

who behaves as usual is Lady Black. She stalks insolently along the top of our garden wall. She looks down
her nose at Tooks—a silent Tooks.

Tooks has brought me as a peace offering his ball,
his far-from-young bone, and laid them at my feet. I
scorn such overtures.

I have offered to get him a kitten for a playmate. The
littlest one would be most suitable.

John says when he hears me: " Don't tease the dog.
Poor fellow! Many a thing a man does for a young
family."

THE COMFORT OF MATERIAL THINGS

HAVE you ever thought of, and been thankful for, the comfort we get in our lives from quite ordinary material things? Just now I am pitying the poor rich folks who, now that summer has come, have no longer a cheery fire to brighten them up in the evenings. We working women who spend so much time in our kitchens have the best of it during these chilly days of so-called summer. Is there anything in the world that so lifts your spirits up and makes you take a brighter view of life than just the sight of a blazing fire? Not necessarily a big fire—but a bright, leaping, dancing one! I can't be doing with the thrifty smouldering fire, all banked up with dross and wet papers and coke. Thrifty it may be—but goodness me! Isn't it cheerless? Now I maintain that a thriftless leaping fire, with maybe a piece of tarry wood in its heart just to give it extra life, is in reality a far thriftier thing than your banked-up smouldering-going-to-sulk-all-night fire. Why? Well look at the cheery fire—doesn't it make you feel glad? Outside it is raining, and the wind is none too warm. Inside there's this lovely leaping thing, and up go your spirits at the sight of it, and you say " Let's have toast for tea; the fire is just right for it." So everyone catches the cheery infection, and forgets all about the weather.

The smoky, sulky fire depresses you, even if you are not cold—you hate its ill-tempered and half-hearted attempts at being a fire, and when at eleven o'clock at night it finally goes out, you say " Well, let it, it has smouldered away all day, and never once blazed." You see, it had failed in its life work, which was first and foremost to spread comfort and cheer, and the only good thing you can say about it is: " It lasted all day." But who wants a sulky person in the house all day? No, no. "A short life but a merry one " applies quite as aptly to fires as to folk. Have you ever heard the superstition that to sit by a dying fire lowers one's own vitality? And old people used to tell us that in a sick room, however small the fire was, provided it were cheery, it helped the patient towards recovery.

Another extremely comforting thing is a singing

kettle. The other evening Mrs. Keith took us in to hear her new gramophone, the one Annie and her husband sent her. They have a number of good records. There is one of a famous prima donna, whose voice goes to an incredible height. I give you my candid word for it, for sheer comfort and cheer the voice of my singing kettle brings me far more pleasure than the high notes and trills of this great singer.

We don't like to think we are greedy, and we own rather shamefacedly to having a " sweet tooth." Have you ever in the course of your morning's work come on a packet of sweeties, tucked away so securely that they were quite forgotten? Can you not recall with what wholehearted and childish delight you ate up these goodies? Yes, you did, even though they looked none too clean, and were decidedly sticky. They were as welcome as " money from home." It was the morning you had been cleaning the flues of the kitchen range, and your throat and eyes and nose were full of soot and dust. The comfort of those sweeties—shall we ever forget it?

There is a funny Spanish proverb which says: " Blessings on the man who invented sleep." Well, I am afraid no human being can *invent* sleep, but we can do things to induce it to come to us, and so I change the proverb into " Blessings on the man who invented beds." Think how sore our bones would be if we had to

34

lie on the floor all night, or even on a fairly soft rug. The comfort of going to bed when you are tired—what is to compare with it? Especially if you have had a big washing that day, and have got all your clothes dried and ironed, and you go to bed bone-weary, and lay your aching body and tired limbs on the mattress, close

BLESSINGS ON THE MAN WHO INVENTED BEDS

your eyes, heave a sigh of sheer satisfaction, and say " Blessings on the man who invented beds."

I have known myself to face a hard day's work quite cheerfully, because I had a clean blouse to wear, and an apron which I had carefully patched myself. The comfort of that neat patch—how it cheered me, especially when I remembered that I didn't want to do it one single bit.

A cup of tea! This is almost more than a material

35

comfort, it is a spiritual one! How I pity the folks who lived in the days before tea was within the reach of all. I was reading the other day of how tea-drinking only became common in our British Navy a hundred years ago. Before that, the Jack Tars drank beer, grog, rum, and far-from-fresh water. Now, the Admiralty issue tea rations as regularly as they did liquor in the old days. You see, the men have learned the comfort of a cup of tea. What tea is to us women is beyond me to tell. I wish I were a poet so that I might sing a song in praise of the teapot!

Comfort a spiritual thing! Oh, yes, I daresay, but commend me to the homely material things, the dancing fire, the singing kettle, the comfortable bed, the packet of sweeties, and the cup of tea!

I remember once hearing a rather falutin' girl say she'd love to strew flowers in the paths of all working women, and a working woman who heard her said with a dry laugh: " They'd thank you better if you strewed comfortably roomy shoes on their way—for mercy me! don't these cobbles and flints make your feet ache? "

Aye, aye, when we count our blessings, don't let's forget the comfort of the homely things!

> " If I have moved among my race
> And shown no glorious morning face;
> If beams from happy human eyes
> Have moved me not; if morning skies,

Books, and my food, and summer rain
Knocked on my sullen heart in vain——
Lord, thy most pointed pleasure take
And stab my spirit—wide awake! "

SUCH A TREAT

THE other day, a friend from the country sent us as a treat a bottle of home-made raspberry wine. When I was a child my Granny used to make it, and I thought it the most delightful beverage in the whole world. She used to keep it in the parlour cupboard, and sometimes, oh, as a great treat, she would invite us into the sacred room, and give us a glass of raspberry wine. I used to think what bliss it would be to have a whole bottleful all to myself; but, of course, that was too wildly impossible! A small wineglassful on very rare occasions, carefully sipped to make it last longer, was the limit.

Thinking of these things, I went for a glass and poured myself out a good helping. The colour was lovely, and the fragrance of ripe rasps filled the room! I had a hundred happy memories as I looked and sniffed.

Then I took a sip. Ah! how deliciously it tasted! I looked at the glass, and thought what a lot of pleasure I was going to get out of this treat. There was no one in the house, and I had a sort of sneaky feeling that I was being greedy in not waiting till John and the boys could join me. Still . . . I took another sip, and smacked my lips. How the taste brought back old days, and memories of my Granny, of her prim old parlour with its flowery chintz and horsehair furniture. Another sip . . . wasn't this wine a little sweeter than it used to be? Another sip, just to make sure. Yes, it was decidedly on the sweet side; I used not to think it too sweet in the old days. Possibly this was a new recipe. The next sip convinced me that it was not only too sweet—it was cloying, and sticky, and syrupy. Why, in the old days, didn't it have a tart flavour? That flavour had gone now; it was nothing but plain, cloying, sticky sweetness!

I set down the glass half empty . . . and came to the sorrowful conclusion that I didn't like it! What had been such a treat in my childhood was a treat no longer. I'd rather have a cup of tea any day!

I was brooding over this, and over my vanished youth, when the boys came home for dinner. Needless to say, they loved the raspberry wine, and took copious draughts of it. As they did so, Jack was speaking, as he always is, of motor cars and motor bikes.

"James Henderson has got a mo' bike," he told us,

" and, poor chap, when the least little thing is wrong with it, his father makes him take it to the motor works to get it sorted. He's never been allowed to take down one single bit of the bike. His father says he's too young. I call it a fair shame! Why, taking down a bike, and cleaning it and oiling it and decarbonizing it, is such a treat! If ever I've a mo' bike, I'll do all the repairing to it myself."

"And ruin it," I said cruelly. Jack frowned, and helped himself to more raspberry wine. " Every boy if he gets a bike, either a push one or a motor one, should be allowed to take it down and put it up again. If he can't, he should jolly well get a pram or a go-cart, for he is a baby still. Can I have one more mouthful of the raspberry wine? It *is* a treat."

Mrs. Keith came to see me in the afternoon, and she was carrying a mysterious looking parcel. " I want to show you what I have been making for Annie's little girl," she said, undoing the paper wrappings. Inside was a dolly, beautifully dressed, the hat trimmed with flowers, an elaborate frock, and real silk socks and kid shoes. Oh, a gorgeous young lady!

We examined the toy, and Mrs. Keith said in a sort of shamefaced way: " I've enjoyed dressing the doll— it was a sort of treat. When I was a little girl I longed for just such a dolly, but I never got it. I'm glad little Nannie is to be luckier than her Granny."

" I'm sure she'll love it," I said. " No child could help adoring such a dolly."

Well, the ghastly thing was that Nannie wouldn't look at the grand doll! She'd a horrid old rag one that she loved and nursed all day and all night, and called

SHE DUMPED IT REMORSELESSLY ON THE FLOOR

her baby. She said the new one was " nashy " and dumped it remorselessly on the floor. Clearly, it was no treat to her.

Treats? . . . What are they? Evidently, they do not belong to any particular age. The raspberry wine had ceased to be a treat to me, because I thought I was too old. James Henderson's motor bike was no treat, because he was too young, and little Nannie didn't care for her grand doll, because she loved the old one better.

Ah, but dig deeper, and we'll find out why these things have ceased to give us pleasure. It was because there was something else in our minds that we loved better. A treat, to be a treat, must have a certain glamour about it. Raspberry wine had for me no glamour. I like tea better. To Jack, the treat of taking down a bike is surrounded with glamour. He sees himself a great engineer. And to little baby Nannie, her rag doll is a beautiful baby. She sees it through a glamour, and that glamour transforms it.

Isn't it a blessing we have these illusions, for " where there is no vision the people perish."

DEPRESSION OVER ICELAND

" DEPRESSION over Iceland," was the weather report the other Sunday evening. Well, far be it from me to grudge Iceland all the depression it wants if it would only keep it to itself. But no such luck! Sunday's depression in Iceland is Monday's depression all over the British Islands, and Iceland might know by this time that Monday is washing day here.

I wonder if any of you noticed quite lately that an Icelandic traveller was in this country. Someone asked him what did he think of Britain. He replied that he thought the climate very depressing. Well, when one remembers that it's from his own country we get our depressions, I think his answer was a bit thick, don't you?

We're having a rug-making competition in our W.R.I. just now, and it's as good a way of getting rid

43

of depression as any I know. One is always wondering how the next little bit of pattern is going to look. It isn't a dear occupation, either. If you unwind all the old socks and stockings and jumpers, buy some cheap dyes and choose your own colours, it's as cheap as it is interesting. The only things one has to buy are the canvas and the bodkin for pulling through the wool.

To begin with, my pattern was to be a row of hollyhocks, but somehow it has now become a fruit tree—a kind unknown to any gardener, for it has growing on it golden oranges, rosy apples, purple things that could be plums of a small size or black currants of a large size. I have visions of making a bird on the topmost branch, a robin, I think, though it may turn out to be a grey parrot with a red tail—one never can tell! That's the joyful part of making a wool rug, you're never sure what's going to happen next.

I'd just finished a most beautiful red apple when *phut!* went my needle. I could have wept! However, that would have wasted time and I wanted to hurry on to see if my next fruit was to be a melon or a grapefruit.

I glanced at the clock. If I were quick I could catch the three-five bus, rush into town, do some shopping, including a new bodkin, and be home by four-thirty. Tooks said he wanted to come too, so after our usual argument about his collar and lead, off we set.

The depression from Iceland was functioning all

right, and the afternoon was dismal. Beside the bus stance there was the usual crowd. I was preparing to cross the street, looking left and looking right and stepping off with my left foot, when there came a sudden cry. Someone clutched my arm and pulled me

TWO ANGRY WOMEN GLARED AT EACH OTHER

back and a voice trembling with terror said: " Oh, *do* take care! Look, *look*! "

I looked. By motor cars I fully expect to be run over some day. Motor bikes fill me with suspicion, and indeed the ordinary push bike is not without its menace; but to be run down by an ordinary pram with a baby inside it was about the last thing I was expecting! And of course Tooks and his lead were mixed up in the confusion! The baby howled, Tooks barked, and two angry women glared at each other. I was one! Then a gentle little voice said: " I do hope no one is hurt. I'll hold the dog's lead while you dust your dresses."

A quiet, white-faced, brown-eyed, little woman was looking anxiously at us—the owner of the voice and of the firm hand that had dragged me out of danger a moment before. " I don't think anyone is hurt," she said, and then she smiled.

The moment she smiled the baby knew she was one of God's angels who had been taking care of him, so he smiled too, seeing which his mother smiled, seeing which I smiled, and there we stood smiling amiably at each other until a policeman came along and told us to " move on."

The little lady was going in my direction, so we clutched hold of each other and of Tooks and managed to reach the other side of the street. I thanked her warmly for what she'd done. I also said that people with prams should be put in prison, only of course I didn't mean that. She gave a cheery little laugh and said: " It's often a mother's only chance of doing her shopping and giving her baby an outing at the same time."

We parted feeling like old friends and though I may

never meet her again the memory of her kind act will abide in my heart as something very precious.

I'd got all the odds and ends I needed, including a pair of silk stockings for my niece Kitty's birthday (price two-and-eleven-three) when I remembered that John wanted some liniment for a troublesome chilblain. I popped into the chemist's and got what I wanted. Coming out I thought I heard the sound of something falling. I glanced hastily at my parcels. They seemed all right, so very selfishly I went on my way, and when I reached home I discovered it was my parcel which had fallen—the silk stockings.

Well, listen, I sent a note enclosing stamps to the shop, and by return of post I got my parcel with the stamps inside!

Depression over Iceland? Who cares for it? So long as there are kind hearts and helpful hands and cheery voices we can snap our fingers at depression. And my next pattern in the rug has turned out to be a beautiful glowing tomato, whose other name is the love-apple.

" FEED THE BRUTE "

Next, after making beds, and keeping a cheery, clean fireside, I place in order of importance—cooking! It has not the romance attached to it which the first two possess. No poet has ever written a lyric to a cook, though there have been plenty of books written for her benefit—Cookery Books. All the same, if a woman wants to keep her husband's love, let her do so by " feeding the brute."

" The way to a man's heart is through his stomach," said some sharp-tongued old cynic. Well, perhaps it's true: perhaps it's not; but this is certainly true, that if you want to *keep* his heart, you must do so via his tummy.

Here's a bit of worldly wisdom I'd pass on to all young wives, and those who are hoping soon to be wives. You have your husband's heart, of course. You want to keep it, don't you? Well, do so by way of his tummy, and the way to reach his tummy is via his nose. Yes, I'd say nose before mouth, for we can smell a thing much more quickly than we can taste it. When your man is coming home for his evening meal, see that the fire is bright and leaping, and prepare for him some dish that has a savoury smell. It need not be anything elaborate—ham and eggs, steak and onions, fried herring, oh, homely cosy things, for men are much more simple than women, and one can reach them through all sorts of easy avenues.

" What a good smell," the Brute will say, opening the door and sniffing.

" Better taste," is the brisk retort of the wise wife.

A homely little thing, you say? Yes, but on quite little insignificant-looking hinges mighty doors swing open and shut, so that we have no right to judge of the importance of anything by its size.

"A hungry man is an angry man," remember that, too, and don't, for goodness sake, ask about the new pair of shoes for Tommy, or the extra school book for Jeannie till the Brute is warmed and fed and comfortable.

Charles Dickens, who knew human nature so well, describes for us a supper party in a wayside inn one bitterly cold rainy evening. The landlord invited the wet travellers into his kitchen. " There's a glorious blaze in the kitchen, I can tell you," he said. And it was true, but what struck the travellers first was the delicious smell which greeted their noses. The landlord took the lid off the iron pot, and out there rushed more of the savoury smell, while a steam hung in a fragrant mist over their heads. He suffered the delicious steam to tickle the nostrils of his guests. At last one of them asked "What is it?"

"It's a stew of tripe," said the landlord, smacking his lips, "and cow-heel," smacking them again, "and bacon," smacking them once more, "and steak," smacking them for the fourth time, "and peas, cauliflowers, new potatoes, and sparrow-grass, all working up together in one delicious gravy." Having come to the climax, he smacked his lips a great many times, and taking a long, hearty sniff of the fragrance that was hovering about, put on the cover again with the air of one whose toils on earth were over.

The Harbour Inn stood almost next to the harbour in a little fishing village. When the men came in tired and cold and hungry from the sea, the Harbour Inn opened its hospitable doors. There was always a good fire, and a kind welcome from the landlord, so hardly a man passed by. The result of these visits to the Inn was, of course, the usual one, hungry children, and miserable homes, and unhappy wives.

Then one day, a quiet looking little woman came to the place. Without taking anyone into her confidence she had a little building erected opposite the Inn, and presently the sign " Fishermen's Welcome " appeared above the door. What did she mean to do? She answered the question in her own way, for when the

THE MOST DELICIOUS SMELL OF HAM AND EGGS

men came home from the sea, one bitterly cold day, they were greeted by the most delicious smell of ham and eggs. It came from the " Fishermen's Welcome " whose doors stood hospitably open, and whose fire was sending out a warm glow. First one man and then

51

another paused and looked in; then they entered, and there was the quiet little woman ready to take their orders. " Ham and eggs? " she asked, " or would they rather tripe and onions, or sausages and mashed potatoes? All these were ready, and they could have tea or coffee."

It was the dawning of a new day for that little village. Hardly a man passed the " Fishermen's Welcome " and the Harbour Inn found itself, to its own great amazement, left almost empty.

Cooking, then, when we look at the issues at stake, is surely one of the most important of " the common tasks and daily rounds," and every girl should realize this. " I can't boil a potato," said Etta Smith, the other evening, and she said it as if it were something to boast about. She is engaged to Jim Gray, a young working engineer. Well, all I can say is, Heaven help them both when they are married, for she is going to put a strain upon her husband's love, which, I am afraid, will break it.

It is said that Napoleon lost the battle of Waterloo because the lunch he ate before going into action consisted of a chop which was very badly cooked. To " Feed the Brute " is surely a task that is worthy of our best efforts.

VINEGAR OR TREACLE?

In spite of all sorts of preventative measures taken in the spring our window panes have an amazing number of flies buzzing around them. Under the ceiling flies circle slowly round and round on sunny days and on damp ones walk on the ceiling. If I leave a morsel of food anywhere, instantly a regular crowd of these horrid pests alights upon it and makes it disgusting.

Tooks has a most violent objection to flies, especially when they buzz. To begin with he was rather amused at them, and used to make playful snaps under the impression that he could catch them, but of course he never did. One sad day he saw in the garden what he thought was an honest-to-goodness fly (rather larger than the usual variety and rather prettier), so he made a snap at it, and what do you think happened? The fly stung him first on the tail and then on the nose, buzzing angrily all the while. You see, the fly turned out to be a wasp, and a particularly bad-tempered one, and it took me most of that day to soothe Tooks' wounded feelings and bathe his swollen nose. Since then the buzzing of any insect sends him scurrying into shelter. Robbie used to say he was so frightened he'd take refuge behind a hen canary. Personally speaking I think this is a bit exaggerated.

But to get back to the question of flies and how to get rid of them: someone told me that flies dislike a through draught. I opened windows and doors, and made the house as uncomfortable as a mountain top in a north-east gale, to see if this would rid me of my unwelcome visitors. Then some other person told me to try putting down a saucer of vinegar, as the flies dislike the smell and hate the taste and so depart in search of something nicer.

Well, I've filled my house with cold draughts; I've filled it full of the smell of vinegar; I've sat shivering in the draught and all I've caught was a cold in the head. The flies seem to be amused; they were certainly not diminished.

Mrs. Keith came in to see me and asked, not unreasonably, why was I sitting in such discomfort, and why the saucers of vinegar? I told her I was clearing the house of flies. She laughed and said: " Try treacle, and close your doors and windows. Flies love the smell and taste of treacle, and they'll come in crowds to sip it. The draughts and the vinegar, even if they do drive them away for a little, don't get at the root of the matter for the flies come back. Try treacle and you'll

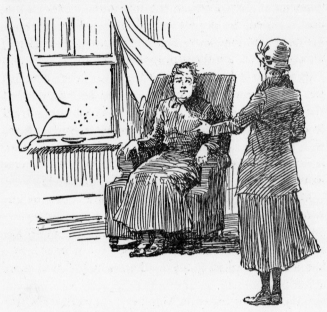

MRS. KEITH CAME IN TO SEE ME

have the flies for 'keeps.' They must 'stay put' for the excellent reason that they can't get out of the sticky stuff, and once you've trapped them then it's easy to destroy them. You'll catch far more flies with treacle than you'll ever do with vinegar."

Thankfully (for I was shivering and sneezing) I closed the windows and doors, emptied the vinegar and filled the saucers with East India best black molasses. Then I poked the fire into a cheery blaze and awaited developments. I hadn't long to wait. First one and then another hungry curious fly alighted, took a sip, then another sip; took a foot bath, then, when they tried to swim, they found the snag! They couldn't free themselves—they were stuck, and how they hated the sticky feeling on their thin legs. In vain they tried to clean them. I couldn't help feeling sorry for them, still, I had to harden my heart, and in about half an hour I was numbering the slain by dozens and then by scores. Yes, treacle, not vinegar, did the trick.

Mrs. Forrest came in next day. She's a new neighbour. Her husband is a carpenter, and is an extraordinarily handy man. Perhaps it's because she brags so much about it that I can't abide the woman. She has a way of ruffling my feathers which I find most irritating.

" We're going away on Monday," she said, " and I'll take the washing house that day, and you can have it on Tuesday. It won't matter, will it? "

My first impulse was to say it *would* matter, and to refuse to give up my day and also to remind her that *she* had been very disobliging when I wanted to change days with her. " Treacle, not vinegar." Mrs. Keith's words came back to me and I said (oh, it required an effort to do it) quite amiably: " Yes, it'll be all right, Mrs. Forrest, and if you like I can let you have my extra clothes line."

She thanked me, but none too graciously, and departed. When John came home he had a very bright face, and was carrying under his arm a mysterious-looking parcel. It was one of these new gadgets for winding up clothes lines, a thing I'd been wanting for ages.

" From Sam Forrest, for you. He made it specially for you, because his wife has been telling him how obliging you've been about the washing house."

I tell you I felt small because I hadn't wanted to be obliging. Quite a lot of us try to clear away our difficulties by vinegary methods. Wouldn't it be a good plan to try the treacle and see what happens? Keep sweet; it pays ever so much better both for ourselves and for those about us.

SOULS AND BODIES

I AM just getting better of my annual bout of influenza
and feeling about as cheery as a foggy day when there's
" depression over Iceland." When I can spare a
moment from pitying myself I feel sorry for John shut
up with such a grumbling wife, and a noisy one as well,
for I keep coughing night and day. The boys took
Tooks back with them after the Christmas holidays so
the house is dull beyond all telling.

" Look here, goodwife," John said, " I'm going to
buy you a bottle of cod-liver oil, to see if it'll stop that
cough. Jim Dalton's wife had a far worse cough . . ."

" She had not," I said angrily, and I coughed as
loudly as I could, just to show how ill I was. " You've
no business to be discussing my cough with Jim Dalton.
You men are no better than a pack of gossiping old
wives."

" I'm going to buy you the oil," John went on

patiently. "There's a new kind this year made in Iceland. . . ."

"Where the depressions come from? "

"Where the very best cods come from," John said, ice in his tones.

"Well, ever so many thanks," I said, trying to be gracious, " but I'll buy it myself; I know you don't like doing shopping."

John admitted he did not and was clearly much relieved that I'd offered to get it; I did not tell him that I knew that if he bought it he'd buy the biggest bottle in the shop and it would take me ages to get through the stuff. I simply hate and detest cod-liver oil. Yes, yes, I know there are excellent and worthy people who love it so much that they put the bottle to their lips, being so impatient that they cannot wait to measure it into a spoon. All honour to these brave souls! I don't mind (much) the taste of the stuff; it's the way it rises triumphantly over everything for the rest of the day that I object to. It makes everything taste and smell of ancient fish.

John, little knowing the amazing artfulness of his wife, laid the money on the table and his parting injunction was " Get it to-day."

. . . . . .

The day was horrid, with a grey unkind sky and a wind at every corner ready to stab you to the heart.

59

Everyone in the bus was as disagreeable as the day. At one stopping place an old woman climbed in. She had her head and shoulders wrapped in an ancient grey shawl, she carried a meagre looking black bag bulging with parcels wrapped in brown paper. Any one more depressing you could not see, yet when someone pushed past her, a parcel fell out of her bag and, lo and behold, we saw it contained a bunch of golden tulips!

You've no idea how the sight of the lovely things in that bus of unlovely folks cheered us and made us feel happy and friendly! In that load of people who had all been buying food and clothes, material things for bodily wants, only one person had remembered to get something with which to feed her soul and that was the old charwoman. Her divine recklessness cheered us all. " Man shall not live by bread alone," says the Old Book; we need other things, such as flowers and birds' songs and children's laughter, if we want to save alive what is far more important than our bodies, namely our souls.

The shop windows were gay with spring goods and I paused to feast my eyes on the windows of Austin the Florist's shop. Have you ever noticed how many spring flowers are the colour of sunshine? Crocuses and daffodils and mimosa and primroses and cowslips. They all look as if they were bits of sunshine and the pleasure they bring us is akin to pain.

Before a brown crock in which were a score or more of gay golden daffodils I stood spellbound. It was such a homely looking crock meant to hold useful things like potatoes or onions, and here it was full of flowers

I STOOD SPELLBOUND

proudly declaring once more that man shall not live by bread or potatoes or onions alone. For the second time in that dismal day I was reminded that we have souls as well as bodies and that we don't pay nearly enough attention to them. If we starved our bodies as we starve our souls what a fuss we'd make!

Of course, I was not to buy that bowl of daffodils—certainly not! I was to buy a bottle of excellent cod-liver oil, the kind that comes from Iceland where the cods (and the fogs) are so special. But it would do no harm to ask the price, would it? Thus, arguing with my conscience or rather with my husband's orders, did I dally with temptation.

The smell of a florist's shop always goes to my head so that I'm really not responsible for my actions. That was how I tried to throw dust in my eyes when five minutes afterwards I emerged, bearing tenderly in my arms—the oil? Not a bit of it—but the crock of golden daffodils! With the pennies over I bought a knot of violets. Now then!

I set my crock on the table to see the effect, then I tried it on the dresser. It looked lovely in either place, but when I set it on the window sill I knew that was the proper place. People passing by could see the loveliness and the daffodils would out of their golden trumpets sing them a song of cheer, of spring and of hope.

My fragrant bunch of violets I have set in a glass dish on the table, and the scent fills the whole house and tells us of young lambs and little birds and fluffy chicks and all the other gladsome things of the coming time.

My cough is gone (probably to Iceland) and my

depression has gone with it. I don't care a hoot what
John will say. I have my daffodils and my daftness:

> " If there is food upon thy shelf
> And naught upon thy sill,
> Fast for a day and buy thyself
> A golden daffodil."

I've bought a whole crockful!

LIGHTS

I'M awfully glad I didn't live in the good old days before
paraffin lamps were invented. In my grannie's house
there was an old crusie lamp, and she has often told us
how in her young days it was all the light they had.
The oil which it burned was made from fish and the
wick was simply a rush. She used to tell us that on
the days when the women of her village were making
oil for the lamps the smell was something sickening! I
can well believe it.

There's something about a dull light which sends
your spirits down to your boots quicker than anything
else I know. Just try keeping a company of people in
a dully lighted room. To begin with they may have
been all " quite full of beans " but in a little while
depression seizes them and quenches their bright

spirits. Bring in a brightly lighted lamp; stir up the fire till it blazes, and you see a miracle. Faces brighten, spirits rise, smiles reappear and laughter is heard. Ah! light is a great magician.

Then, is there anything cheerier than to walk down a street of gaily-lighted shop windows? Your own spirits catch the gaiety which is in the air and you go home feeling that life isn't such a dismal affair after all. I adore a shop that's lighted by electric lights. The man who invented this way of lightening our darkness deserves a royal decoration. I would also remember with gratitude the shopkeepers who give us this pleasure.

And what about our own homes? Have we always a good lamp on the table? Do those of us who use paraffin lamps take trouble to trim the wicks and polish the glasses? It's the woman's job, remember. Do we, in our zeal for thrift, keep our lobbies in darkness? This also is a point for the woman of the house to decide.

I can't be bothered with the thrifty woman who, if she is going out for half a minute, screws down her lamp till the flame is a mere pin-point. She may save a few drops of oil (though I doubt it) but she makes the spirits of those who have passed by her darkened windows sink down. She has added a little more depression to the burden of the already depressed. Is this real thrift? After all we cannot measure things— the best things—by a mere material measure.

We all know the pleasant feeling we experience when, on some dark night, we tap at a door and immediately when it is opened out streams a flood of warm light. The light warms our hearts too and makes us feel that the folks in the house are glad to see us. But if, when the door is opened, there's only a distant light from the kitchen and an equally distant voice asks "Who's there?" we feel chilled to the bones. The determining feature in both cases was first and foremost the light. In the one case we were cheered; in the other we were depressed.

"Is it worth while that we jostle a brother,
Bearing his load on the rough road of life?"

If I lived in a house where the electric light can be had by merely touching a button, I would have my street door always lighted. Yes, I would, and thrift be hanged! Voyagers on the sea of life going up and down the street would see my light and would feel cheered. Also they would notice that stone which nearly broke my own nose during the dark days of the War when we weren't allowed lights. There would be no need to cry "Mind that step," for the light would in a far kinder and more effective way give them warning.

Suppose light-houses took a leaf out of the pages of the "thrifty" housewife and said: "To-night it's dark and cloudy; all nice respectable ships should be in port. We'll not light the lamp and waste the oil." What do you think would happen? It's possible that nothing might happen but it's also possible and very probable

OUT STREAMS A FLOOD OF WARM LIGHT

that some ship might go to wreck on the rocks and that lives might be lost.

Charles Dickens believed in the wisdom of lighted lamps and cheery windows. His stories are full of

67

reference to them. He is continually noticing and telling his readers that the fire was burning brightly, the hearth was swept and the lamp was blazing. Do you remember how in one of his stories he tells us about an old fisherman and how he believed in the lighted lamp? This rough old chap who had a heart of gold used to light a lamp and place it in the window where its light shone over the dark sandy waste outside. " ' Theer! ' said Mr. Peggotty, cheerily. ' Lighted up, accordin' to custom! You're a wonderin' what that's fur, sir! Well, it's fur our little Emily. You see, the path ain't over light or cheerful arter dark; and when I'm here at the hour as she's a comin' home, I puts the light in the winder. That, you see,' said Mr. Peggotty, bending over me with great glee, ' meets two objects. She says, says Emily, " My uncle's theer! " ' "

Years afterwards, when poor Emily had made shipwreck of her life, the lighted flame of her uncle's love showed her the way home once more. One cannot help wondering, if old Peggotty had saved the light would he ever have saved little Emily? There's such a thing as divine waste!

It was during the dismal dark years of the War that we realized how much our neighbours' lighted windows had meant to us. It is good for us sometimes to think of these times, " Lest we forget, Lest we forget."

CRISES

HAVE you ever thought that when one crisis in our lives is passed we just get ready for another? We say, and we think it's true, " When this crisis is past we'll have peace for ever," and behold number one is barely past when number two comes tripping round the corner.

As the years go on those crises seem to come more quickly than when we were younger. Life, like a river nearing the sea, becomes more crowded and crises simply jostle each other. Yet people will tell you that life is monotonous and that one day is just like another. Nay, that is not so, for all during our lives a changing process is going steadily on.

We women always think that when we are married we'll settle down. My word, that's a pretty bad mistake.

It's when we marry things begin to happen. You remember Harry Lauder's funny song where he says " I'll try to settle up, and then I'll settle down." But how to settle down, that is the question. Presently we are busy preparing for the baby whose coming is to make our home complete. " I'll settle down, now," I remember saying after Jack's birth, and why, I was hardly out of bed when I began deciding what I'd do with this wonderful son of mine. He was to be a great man, of course—a captain in the army or a master of men and of works—a Member of Parliament, oh, there were no limits to his greatness! Later on I prayed that my boy might be a good man—that first—and that did not come until I had passed through many crises.

School days! " When the children are in school we'll have a quiet time." Well, if we want to help our children with their lessons school days are nearly as strenuous for the parents as for the children. I remember wrestling with compound interest and problems till I was nearly dead with brain fever. And as for fractions, they are a mystery to me to this day.

School days ended, the crisis past—does rest come now? In many ways the crisis we come to now is one of the most painful. The young birds are leaving the nest and the old ones are trying to fill in the time till they come back again. And they only come home for a holiday now—not for keeps! Already for them the kingdom round the corner is beckoning and the home nest cannot keep them.

I remember when Jack was little his father and myself managed by saving our pennies to buy a little second-hand bicycle for him. He was terribly proud of it and learned to ride it very quickly. He said to me one day: " I used to wonder would I ever get a bicycle; and I've got one and I can ride it and it's all come true, and now I'm wondering what it will feel like to ride a motor bicycle." You see? One crisis making way for another.

I suppose when my sons choose wives that will be a terrible crisis. I must remind myself that their father did the same when he chose me. Looking back at it now I wonder was I, in this crisis, as kind to John's mother as I might have been? Youth is prone to be thoughtless and selfish. Now that I'm looking forward to this big crisis in my own life, I wonder how did I conduct myself when the crisis was in my mother-in-law's life. One thing I cannot bear and that is jokes about mothers-in-law. I'm sensitive on the subject already.

So life goes restlessly on. All crises aren't the same size. After the spring cleaning, for instance, which we women call a minor crisis and our husbands a major one, we settle down in peace and quietness for a little, but it's only for a little. Life, like a river, has little quiet backwater streams in it, and I always think the lull after the spring cleaning is like the quiet of one of these little streams. But presently the current quickens, the stream rushes on and we are borne along to our next crisis. Still, let us remember and be thankful that we have had a little breathing space.

There is an old story told that when God made man He poured out for him all the good things He could think of. Health and wealth and beauty and honour—oh, all that could make life beautiful He poured out for the benefit of mankind. There was just one thing He did not give, and that was *rest*. " If I give him rest," said God, " he will never seek Me, so I shall keep it." It's an interesting old story and gives one much to think about. Suppose our present crisis was to be our last and after that a long spell of quietness, how quickly we should begin to complain of the monotony of our existence.

Just now the domestic crisis which will be facing us is the making of marmalade. It is a crisis to which we look forward with pleasure. We know that after it comes the crisis of the spring cleaning. But in the meantime, during these dark cold days the handling of the golden fruit, the delicious smell of the oranges and lemons, is almost as good as a trip to sunny Spain.

I was in the other day with Mrs. Keith who was making chutney and I sat entranced watching the various things she used. If any of you want a trip to

India—just get busy making chutney. It will be a crisis and a very pleasant one.

And so through all the year we will pass through crisis after crisis. The older we grow the more quickly do they come or possibly it seems so to us. No two crises

THE MAKING OF MARMALADE

are alike any more than any two days are alike. One of our poets has said:

"When earth's last pictures are painted,
And the tubes are twisted and dried,
When the oldest colour has faded,
And the youngest critic has died,
We shall rest. . . ."

The poet means that all our crises are behind us and the time has come to rest.

73

CABBAGE *OR* POTATO

You remember the story of the careful housewife who was one Sunday entertaining the minister to dinner? After helping him to cold boiled mutton she asked, " Cabbage or potato? "

The guest replied, " Cabbage *and* potato."

Personally I have always felt sorry for the poor man yet I don't know if my sorrow was justifiable. Perhaps both vegetables would have upset him; perhaps had he decided to have only one he would have escaped the fit of indigestion which was otherwise coming to him.

What's wrong with quite a lot of us is that when life asks us " Cabbage or potato?" we reply "Cabbage *and* potato " and are very sorry when we find out that we can't have both without suffering for our greed.

I think it is an American writer who has told us of a man who one day met an angel.

" I will give you whatever you want," said this obliging and heavenly visitor. " Then," said the man. " I'd like my lost youth."

" You shall have it."

" I'd like my wife too," said the man.

" Your wife? " asked the angel.

" Yes, and oh, please, couldn't I have my boys and girls as well? "

The angel laughed. " Why, you can't be a boy and have a wife and family too."

It's just another version of " Cabbage and potato."

I went in to see Mrs. Scott the other day, and found her making a roly-poly for dinner, using syrup as a filling. " Jam would be nicer," said I, "why don't you use it?"

" Because I don't happen to have any," she answered. " I was nursing George through the scarlet fever when the berries were ripe. Well I'm glad to have my man back to his work again even if I have no jam."

A wise woman, wasn't she? She had made her choice and was prepared to abide by it. When life had asked her whether she had rather nurse her husband or make a few paltry pots of preserves she made her choice wisely.

I was pondering over her words when I went to dust the ornaments in my best room. I call it my parlour; I suppose this is a hopelessly old-fashioned word. My cousin Barbara (who has more money than sense) sent me for my last birthday a beautiful little Chinese cabinet. It has lacquer doors and silver hinges and is a sheer joy to behold. The one place where I could put it was on the mantelpiece, and I could only find room for it by moving from its place of honour the brown lustre jug of English pottery which I had inherited from my Aunt Jean. Loath to hide away my jug, and yet not having room for it, what do you think I did? I set it on the top of my cabinet.

Now, the queer thing is that both cabinet and jug are beautiful. Yet when I put them together they looked ugly. The brown lustre was not the same shade as the Chinese lacquer; the top of the cabinet made the jug look top heavy, and the whole arrangement offended my eyes. Yet, greedy woman, I said " Cabbage and potato, please." I got both and got a fit of indigestion for my pains. China and old England shrieked at each other!

Not without a sigh and a word of apology to my jug I took it off its all-too-narrow resting place. I laid it carefully away in the top of a cupboard. The decision caused me a pang, but it was worth it, for now I can see the beauty of the cabinet. More than that, John said last Sunday, " That's a pretty thing you have on the parlour mantelpiece. I don't think I ever saw it before." I told him reproachfully it had been there since my last birthday. "I never noticed it," he said.

By and by I shall hide it away and take out my jug, and the same thing will happen. "Cabbage or potato?" Life is continually asking us which will we have.

Before marriage we women demand of life that it shall

A BABY IS A WHOLE-TIME JOB

give us everything, love and a home and children and a good time and friends. Well, we can't have everything. If we are going to have all the fun we had before marriage something has got to be sacrificed. We can't attend to our home and children and gad about too.

F

A baby, for instance, is a whole-time job, and no woman worth her salt will hesitate for a moment when she weighs her child in the balance against pleasure. The child has it every time; the mother scarcely notices that she has made her decision, it is so much a matter of course.

From the beginning of life right on to the end we are daily and hourly deciding whether we will have " Cabbage *or* potatoes." We can't have both. What we can have is the power to select which we think the more important. You remember the old fable of the dog who was trotting over a foot bridge with a fine big bone in its mouth? In the water he saw reflected another dog with a bigger bone in its mouth. Immediately the first dog dropped its bone and grabbed at the one in the water, only to find that it had lost the substance in reaching out for the shadow. It's tragic when life asks of us to choose which we will have, and we make a mess of things by our unwise choice. Life is, after all, a long game of selection, of settling for ourselves whether we shall have " Cabbage *or* potatoes."

READY MADES

WHEN we buy a ready-made garment we are always quite willing that it should be altered to fit us. It's sure to be either too long or too short or needing something done to the collar or the sleeves. This altering is a bother, of course, but we put up with it knowing that these alterations will make the garment fit and suit us.

Well, now, do we do this with our opinions? Do we take them ready made and clap them on our minds and never give another thought as to how they fit? If we do I'm here to say that the minds of quite a lot of us must look perfect freaks running about in those ready-made garments which fit them so badly. We hate our bodies to look odd and badly clad. Why, on earth, shouldn't we be equally careful about our minds?

The answer is—Pure Laziness! We can't be bothered. It's too much trouble to do our own thinking. It's much easier to take our opinions ready made, and never mind about the fitting. Women, even more than men, are slaves to these ready-made opinions.

Take, for instance, that old misleading and most unflattering opinion which we hear so often: " Women talk much more than men." Is this true? Does this opinion fit the facts of the case?

Sit in a room with a lot of men, and though you may be the only woman in it, you'll be lucky if you can get a word in edgewise now and then. Oh, that old, ready-made opinion about our strong, silent men is rubbish. Strong they may be, but silent they certainly are not.

Listen to the laughter that greets the one who says to you, " You're very quiet to-night. Isn't that unusual? Aren't women generally talking? " The speaker (he has been holding forth eloquently for the last half hour) has got firmly planted in his mind that old untruthful opinion that women talk more than men, and nothing short of an earthquake will make him change his mind.

There's another ready-made opinion I'd like to draw your attention to. It's believed in by both men and women. It's a badly fitting "ready-made"! It is that women drink more tea than men. I'd like to alter this opinion and say that men are quite as fond of tea (and talk) as women.

Can you tell me, my sister women, when did you ever have a cup of tea in which your husband wasn't more than willing to join you?

I remember Mrs. Keith telling me that her husband always protested he didn't like tea. He'd have an early cup, however, just to please her and to keep her company. So one morning she drank her tea and didn't say a word to him. She popped the teapot into the oven when she heard him coming downstairs. He pretended he was looking for a bootlace or an extra stud or some such feeble excuse, and she helped him. At last, in desperation, and when he saw that she wasn't going to mention it, he faltered, "Aren't you having an early cup of tea this morning? " She said she'd had it, but knowing that he only took it to please her she had put the teapot away. If he was looking for it he'd find it in the oven. It was soon *out* of the oven and its contents poured into a cup. He never said again that it was only women who drank tea. You see that was a ready-made opinion which he altered and got to fit his mind.

Another ready-made opinion which we women often hear and to which we have submitted far too long is that men are the superior sex. They will say of a thing done by a woman, " Oh, it wasn't bad *for a woman*."

They infer that if they had done it it would be ever so much better. A badly-fitting ready-made and *shoddy* opinion is this.

I remember once Jack taking home with him for a weekend a chum of his. He was quite a nice boy, though his mind was clothed in ill-fitting opinions. His name was Charlie Bridge. He was a handsome lad, and looked well in a posh suit of plus-fours with beautifully knitted hose to match.

He perched himself on the sitting-room table, cigarette in mouth, and legs swinging to and fro. Molly Ross happened to come in. She is now a tall, sweet-faced girl, and perhaps the fact that she was sitting listening to him helped Charlie to spread himself rather more than was necessary. He was no end of a fellow! He gave his opinion of football matches, of motoring, of aeroplanes, and so on. It was just then that he noticed Molly's eyes fixed with great interest on his legs, and for some strange reason he began to feel uncomfortable. Was anything wrong? Why was she looking so intently? He stole a glance—and then— his leg-swinging ceased, his eloquence also ceased and trickles of icy cold water began to run down his spine and to take all the cockiness out of him. What had happened?

Right in the very middle of the leg of his stocking was a *hole*—and the stitches were running with dreadful regularity in a ladder down his leg.

Charlie's firm opinion that he belonged to the superior sex got a horrid jolt just then. He wasn't quite sure but that Molly was laughing at him.

I remember when we were first married John gave

HE WAS NO END OF A FELLOW!

it as his opinion that every wife should fold her husband's Sunday clothes and write his letters. He doesn't hold that opinion now. It was a badly-fitting one and had to be scrapped. It couldn't even be altered to fit.

PLANT NOW

THE rain was falling with a certain grim determination. " I'm to stay all day," it seemed to say. Our bus was full to overflowing of large fat men and women all carrying dripping umbrellas, large baskets and horrid bulgy parcels. We were all cross too, and cold and miserable, and we felt furious when some belated traveller waved his umbrella at us as a sign that he wanted to board the bus.

I was seated next the window and just to pass the time I rubbed the moisture off the glass and looked out. We were in front of Ferguson the Seedsman's shop, and in great red letters all across his windows were written these words, " PLANT NOW."

There was something so hopeful, so cheery and so inspiring in this slogan that I found myself getting hopeful and cheery too just by looking at those windows. " Plant now for spring blooming " was written in smaller print. There were bundles of grey-green looking bushes; but wrapped up inside their grey-greenness were all sorts of lovely things, beautiful blossoms and exquisite perfumes. There were coloured pictures of the rose bushes in bloom. Well, of course, no garden that ever bloomed can match with the coloured (paper) garden blooming on the front of a packet of seed, and no mere early flowering rose tree has ever been so covered with lovely roses and buds as is the coloured advertisement in the seedsman's catalogue. Still!—one never knows what may happen next spring. Here's hoping!

Roses—red roses—to bloom in May; white roses in June; damask roses—maiden's blush—moss and cabbage roses. Aren't these very names full of magic? What could be more wonderful than to be told that in order to have roses like these one must PLANT NOW? Dreary and dismal the weather may be, but it has its use for it is suitable for planting roses now.

Our bulbs are all sending up green shoots indoors, but our gardens are dismal beyond words. Well, they need be dismal no longer for if we plant now they will become to us a source of immediate pleasure.

I drew my neighbour's attention to this cheery slogan of " PLANT NOW." She sighed, moved her dripping umbrella from her own feet to mine and said, " If you

85

want to throw away good money you'll go and buy rose bushes now."

"Well, I don't care; I'm going to buy a couple of bushes; a cabbage and a damask. I like these names; there's such a fine old-fashioned flavour about them," I said, clinging to my " PLANT NOW " cheeriness.

When the bus landed us at our destination I was feeling quite gay. I went into Gray & Saunders to buy new winter woollies for my men folk. Can any one tell me why men's woollies should be of such ugly colours? "Natural wool," the shopman told me. "And unnatural ugliness," I murmured. Yet because of that cheery command to " PLANT NOW " I didn't feel so depressed as I usually do when buying what is known as " Gentlemen's oddments."

" Rather dreary weather," said the shopman, as he was wrapping up my purchases (which, strange to say, came to less than I had expected—a most unusual experience).

" Oh, it's not so bad," I said cheerfully. " Did you notice that in Ferguson the Seedsman's they have got their consignment of rose bushes and are advising people to ' PLANT NOW ' if they want early roses."

The man's face lit up in the most delightful way.

" That does cheer me," he said. " I didn't know the plants had arrived. I'm to get some tea roses from them this year," and then and there he launched into a long discourse as to the soil, the depth of the hole for the root, the manure, and finally offered to come and help me to plant my rose trees.

"But I haven't planted them yet," I stammered. "I haven't even bought them yet; as a matter of fact I'm on my way to the shop just now."

HE LAUNCHED INTO A LONG DISCOURSE

I saw him give an anxious look at the clock on the opposite wall. He seemed to think that every moment wasted over "Gentlemen's oddments" was ruining my chance of those roses which must be planted now.

"A heavy soil," he said, accompanying me to the door, "and plant one or two together. They're like children and get on best when they have young companions."

87

We parted as if we'd known each other for years. Our mutual love for flowers formed a bond. " PLANT Now " not only for flowers but for friendship.

When I was buying my rose bushes I asked the young shop assistant to choose me reliable trees of the cabbage and of the damask order, and I have no words with which to describe the pains that nice boy took to get me just what I wanted. And he wrapped them up in moss and soft paper as if they were babies—and indeed so they are.

I nursed them all the way home and they spoke to me of springtime and summer and birds' songs so that the night, though it was still pouring, no longer depressed me.

It's good to think the world isn't dead in winter; it's only sleeping, and the command to " PLANT Now " proves that presently it will waken up and show us the beauties of summer. Cheer up, then, all despondent hearts. Buy rose bushes, plant them now, and you'll have a foretaste of summer.

LOOK UP

IN a certain eastern city a lame beggar used to be carried and laid down at the door of a church. People going out and coming in used to give him money; sometimes they put it into his outstretched hands, and sometimes they threw it on the ground so that he could gather it up himself. Because of this the man's eyes were often on the ground; he was afraid he might lose even one little coin.

One afternoon about three o'clock he noticed two tall strangers approaching the church door. They were dressed like fishermen and had the open, out-of-doors kind of face of such men. Immediately the lame beggar asked for a copper.

The older of the strangers—a man with a rugged, kindly face—looked intently at the poor cripple. But ... he did not put his hand into his purse; seeing which the beggar, much disappointed, was just going to look down again or along the street in search of someone more generous.

" Look up," cried the fisherman. "Look at us." His voice was ringing. " Silver and gold have I none, but such as I have give I unto thee." He took the lame man by the right hand and immediately a miracle happened for the lame man received strength and walked! Not only did he walk, he leaped!

Silver and gold he had imagined were the most wonderful things in the world. He had asked for them and got something far better. That man would never forget the first words uttered by the strange fisherman, " Look up." No more looking down to the grubby street in search of stray coins. " Look up " into the faces of friends who can give you something far more precious than money. Those words, " *Look up* " are the key-note of the whole story.

A lovely story it is too—you will remember that the fishermen's names were Peter and John and that their meeting-place with the beggar was at the Gate Beautiful, a fitting name for such a beautiful story.

Why am I telling you this story? I'm not telling it to you wholly, but to myself, and I want to emphasise the words, " Look up," for these last few days I've been looking down into the mire and clay of the street and forgetting to lift up mine eyes unto the hills from whence come strength and help.

The new neighbours who have come to live at the back of our house are horrid thoughtless people. They made a huge bonfire of all the rubbish (and a fine lot they had!) and the smoke of it filled our house and made it unpleasant to live in. I couldn't open doors or windows, and what was even worse, our little garden was filled with pieces of half-burned paper and charred cardboard boxes. If you know of anything that looks more horrid and squalid just let me hear of it.

Then John, to whom I had given a beautiful tube of shaving soap, has been annoying me. Instead of squeezing the paste from the end of the tube the wretch has been squeezing it from the top and he'll never get the good of the soap this way. Besides it looks so untidy—I—I could slap him! Why on earth do people do silly things like that? Couldn't he *see* that the tube should be squeezed from the bottom?

Then Tooks has been annoying Mrs. Keith's cat, and although I know that he's a little rascal, he's *my* dog, and I can't bear people finding fault with him, and so on and so on. Every woman who does me the honour of reading on so far will know what she's had to endure of petty worries and annoyances this very day.

Well, I'm here to say, " Look up." And I'm saying it to myself first. Never mind that bonfire; away on the distant hills men are burning last year's heather and the smell of the greenwood is heavenly and makes you think of all sorts of lovely things. That tube of shaving soap—a mere trifle. Next time you buy him shaving soap buy a stick. Why worry when away down by the river-side the trees are already fluffy with pussy-willows in grey-green dresses, and a wren, shyest and daintiest of our wild birds, is getting so excited about her new house that you can see her darting in and out all day. " Look up," then.

As for badly behaved cats and dogs, laugh at them. Like human beings they get into mischief when they're idle. " Satan finds some mischief still for idle dogs to do." Take Tooks out for a long walk. " Look up," lift up your eyes and it will follow quite naturally that the rest of you will rise up too, so that you can leap and walk.

There was once another poor burdened man who was looking for treasure in the mud. He had a rake in his hand and he was bending anxiously, searching, searching in the mire. He kept his eyes and his whole attention on the mud. He hadn't a moment to look up, and the pity of it was that right behind him stood a Shining One holding in his hand a golden crown. If only the man would " Look up."

Well, for my own part, I'm going to try to follow the example of the lame beggar who looked up, and not

SEARCHING, SEARCHING IN THE MIRE

that of the poor deluded creature bending over the muck rake. I've an idea that by looking up the reward will be greater than any silver or gold.

CONSIDER THE POSTAGE STAMP

THE wayside pulpit hanging on the outside of our church has often given the passers-by help and inspiration for their day's work. Time and again it has given us, too, food for thought, with its happy knack of putting some old truths in a new and attractive dress.

This week's message is, " Consider the postage stamp, and stick it." A homely enough text, isn't it? Everyone of us knows the importance of the stamp—knows, too, the supreme importance of the stamp sticking to its job till its destination is reached.

Can't we remember the reproachful way in which we upbraided " Postie " when he drew our attention to an understamped letter. We had to pay double because someone else was careless. I remember hearing about Mrs. Skinner who once lived in this street in the days when stamps were a penny each. One day she got a

94

letter and it had no stamp. She refused to pay the necessary twopence, and ordered the postman to keep it to himself. Afterwards, she thought better of it; the letter might be valuable; so she hurried after " Postie " to trade two jam jars for her letter!

The other evening (Friday to be exact) was our W.R.I. I had attended the first few meetings with exemplary regularity, but on this particular night I thought I'd take a holiday. It was a cold, dark evening, with an east wind at every corner as sharp as a knife. Inside the house the fire burned cosily; my chair by the hearth looked very inviting; I had a new magazine. John, on the other side of the hearth, was deep in his newspapers, and Tooks was lying luxuriously on the hearth-rug. No, certainly not, I was not going out this evening. The boys' last letter was lying on the table— presently I'd reply to it.

" I'm not going out to-night," I said, sitting down contentedly in my chair, and giving the fire a little poke. John grunted—Tooks snored—I turned the pages of my book and listened to the wind howling outside.

Silence filled the room, but presently I became aware of a little voice in my heart. It said, " Consider the postage stamp and stick it."

" Be quiet," I said. Well, would you believe it, no sooner was this voice silent than the clock took up the matter. " Stick it, stick it, stick it," it said solemnly.

" You aren't considering the postage stamp that sticks it. Suppose *all* the members were like you there would be no meetings."

" Isn't the clock very noisy to-night? " I asked my goodman. He said, " Not more than usual," and went on with his reading. Then my eye lighted on the boys' letter. The stamp on the envelope looked sternly at me. " Supposing I did not stick it, you'd have got no letter this week, and then you'd be in a state. . . ."

" John," I said suddenly, " I think I'll go to the W.R.I. after all. If I hurry I'll be in time."

He looked up with a laugh. " Leave the matchbox with me," he pleaded, " my own is empty." Isn't that just like a man? They think of nothing but their comfort.

I rushed forth telling those various fault-finding voices that I hoped they were pleased now, and one of them said, " The surest sign of old age is when a woman prefers her own fireside chair to going out to a meeting."

As I passed Mrs. Keith's door she hurried out after me. " I was listening for your footsteps," she said. " If you weren't going, neither was I. What a cold night."

" It's not so bad once you're out," I replied, speaking in a hardy, hearty voice. " Here, catch hold of my arm and we'll battle along." At the corner of our street we encountered Mrs. Douglas. She also had been in two minds as to whether she would go or not. " But

I love those meetings," she said. "They make a bright break in the week." Knowing the dreary life she leads with a husband out of work and a lot of little folk to attend to, I was glad we called for her.

" IT'S NOT SO BAD ONCE YOU'RE OUT "

There weren't many members out. The demonstration was on making a child's new winter coat out of a woman's old skirt. There were so few of us we were quite a family party, and gathered round the demonstrator watching her clever fingers. I told of the awful time I had had trying to cut out a collar and how Mrs. Keith had helped me. This emboldened Mrs. Keith to show us how she'd done it, and Mrs. Douglas said she had an old tweed skirt but she didn't know how to set about making a coat for her little Daisy.

The end of the matter was that Mrs. Keith promised to help, and I said if they'd both come to my house I'd do the machining. And all this came to pass, with the result that little Daisy Douglas, looking the picture of cosiness, trots past to school every morning. Her mother says she's never had a winter when she was so well clad.

" Consider the postage stamp " then, my sister women, and let us this winter, if we join guild or association or club or anything that is for mutual help and cheer——STICK IT.

MY FIRST FIRE

SUMMER has come at last! Every woman of us knows it in her own peculiar way. For some of us it means that the children have to be coaxed indoors at night. "How can it be bedtime yet and the sun shining?" they ask. For others of us it means long, happy hours cleaning the green fly off the rose trees, or picking the caterpillars off the cabbage.

When we go indoors our houses don't seem so friendly as they do in winter. We do all our cooking on the gas ring or the gas cooker, and go in largely for cold food. Every woman in Pennycook Lane except myself is busy making rhubarb jam; they also stew the rhubarb and insist upon their families partaking largely of it. " It's good for you," they say. Why must things that are good for you be horrid too?

The sitting-room is still solemn and tidy-looking with its starched curtains and chair backs which we used to call tidies. The place smells of turpentine and floor polish and brunswick black, and the fireplace is full of flowers and artificial grass.

I don't know how it is, but the sight of a fireplace thus decorated when I come in late on a summer evening fills me with depression! I may not be cold, I admit, but a grate full of ferns or paper roses or artificial grass just about breaks my heart.

How can you sit beside a fireplace and mend torn clothes or tackle bravely the week's darning? How can you write welcome letters to your friends when every time you lift your eyes from the paper you see a fireplace full of . . . flowers! How can you enjoy reading the nicest paper if, forgetting that it's summer, you stretch out your feet and encounter the cold, unsympathetic feel of a flowerpot?

I don't know how you feel about doing your sewing and mending out of doors, but frankly speaking I can't do a stitch! How can I when the reel runs off and the threads get tied up into knots? And besides, there's a blackbird singing somewhere and I must listen to his delicious fluting. A starling is doing stunts in the birds' bath, and a bold robber bee is plundering the honeysuckle of its riches, and making a great fuss about it.

GYPSIES ARE THE BEST FIRE-BUILDERS
IN THE WORLD

There are so many things to look at—nice things—besides one's work.

Reading a book is beset by the same difficulties. I've never tried, and if I know my own heart I never will try, to write letters out of doors, and so, if those things are to be done, they must be done indoors, and we must invite the Gay Comrade to bear us company.

Joyfully we gather up that unhappy substitute for the fire—the artificial flowers and grasses, and bundle them out of sight.

Gypsies are the best fire-builders in the world. Their plan is to get a lot of little things first, like leaves, straw, shavings, and place over these thin twigs and sticks, then thicker sticks, and finally a log. Then they set fire to the whole caboodle.

For folks who aren't gypsies, paper and firewood do very well, and when I lighted my fire last night I took a fat little junk of wood which had once been part of an apple tree, and set it in an honoured place in the middle of my fire.

How it blazed and crackled and leapt! And up went my spirits with it. As the fire grew, my sense of comfort and of comradeship grew too. Do you remember how the man in the Bible cried, "Aha, aha, I'm warm, I've seen the fire"? The very sight of the fire did him good. It warmed his chilled spirit as well as his chilled body.

When, later on, John came in, he looked surprised and pleased. "A fire? " he said. " Where's my slippers? Oh, here they are in the fender."

Tooks flung himself down in front of the blaze, and looked with happy eyes into the fire. Mrs. Keith, coming to borrow a blouse pattern, said, " Have you a fire? I think I'll go home and light mine."

I was reading the other day a report in the newspaper which told us that nearly all our troubles come from the domestic chimney. Factory chimneys, it seems, aren't nearly so dangerous. Central heating and electric light were recommended, if we were to be a healthy nation. Well, perhaps we may be healthy, but I'm here to say we won't be happy! What happy companionship could folks have sitting round a radiator, for instance? Can you imagine people telling each other secrets and being confidential sitting beside an electric fire? Can you imagine a child drawing in a " creepie " to sit beside a radiator? And what, I ask you, is to become of all our pictures in the fire? Are the bairns to be robbed of these?

There is, too, the problem of the children's saint, Santa Claus. How is he to fill stockings if he cannot come down chimneys?

And on Saturday night when the washing tub is placed in front of the blazing kitchen fire, and the towels are set to warm on the back of a chair, what price our central heating then? As child after child is scrubbed " heads and all " and the clean Saturday nightie pulled over its head, and there is a little pause for a bedtime story—what are we to do? Central heating? Electricity?

John and I sat long over the fire, and we talked of all sorts of happy things, and when at last we went to bed, John said, " That cheery fire tempts one to sit by it." So it does, and one is all the better for sharing an hour or two with the Gay Comrade.

SABBATH DAY—A DAY DIFFERENT

WHAT's the good of a Sabbath day? This question was asked by the French people in the end of the eighteenth century. France had thrown off her old form of government, the King and his counsellors had gone, old laws and old customs had vanished, until at last the reformers came to the day of rest, and they said it must go too. A rest every seventh day? Nonsense. A day to worship God every week? There was no God, they said; they had instead a Goddess of Reason, and she said that the Sabbath day was a mistake; it must go. If people wanted a rest, once in every ten days was enough.

To begin with the French people thought this a fine arrangement. Workmen " carried on " for nine days instead of six. Working women did the same, and then, after a bit, they all discovered that to work for so long without " a day different " was beginning to sap their strength. They could not go on with their work. The seventh day taken out of their wheel of life put all the rest of the machinery out of gear. So they clamoured, and got their Sabbath day back. The Goddess of Reason wasn't satisfactory either; mankind needed the day of rest; they also needed God given back to them.

Have we ever stopped to think what our lives would be like without this " day different? " I do not say a " day of rest;" for the housewife Sunday is no day of rest, but it's " a day different," a day we could ill part with; a day, in fact, like a pivot upon which everything turns during the days of the week that follows. I like to think of it as the first day of the week, and I have still the old-fashioned belief that "A Sabbath well-spent means a week of content." Suppose we were like the French of the Revolution; that our men worked for nine days, that our children went to school for the same time, what a muddle we would get into. Take such a homely thing as the changing of our under-garments: Sunday morning is essentially the day for this, as it is the day for a fresh tablecloth, and fresh towels. Sunday morning is the day we have ham and eggs for breakfast, and we all sit down at the same time. It is the only time in the week we have breakfast altogether. How we would miss all these homely little things, and the quiet glow in our hearts when we remember " This is Sunday, we needn't hurry." I am speaking of the men and children, mind, when I speak of no hurrying, for to us women Sunday may be " a day different," it's certainly not a day of rest. But here's the difference between Sunday and Monday—on Monday everyone is cross, everything is lost, and everyone is in a hurry, but on Sunday there is a lovely calm feeling in the air, and weary men and women feel their spirits soothed by the quiet of the Sabbath day.

There is another thing Sunday does for us, and that is the influence it has upon our clothes. If we had no Sunday, we wouldn't bother about having a Sunday dress, and only a woman knows what it means to change from her working garments into her Sunday ones. When a woman ceases to have a Sunday dress, things are looking pretty serious for her. She had better stop and ask herself what's to be the end of this. A Sunday dress means to her her own self-respect, and that is a treasure to be guarded carefully. To get slovenly about it is the beginning of not bothering about going to church. " I can't go to church," she says, " I haven't a Sunday dress," and the habit grows with tragic rapidity.

I used to watch with great interest a family who sat in front of us in church—a father and mother, two sons and one daughter. They were regularly in their places, decent, respectably dressed working folks. Then the older son ceased to come, and presently the mother ceased also. I did not know them, and as they looked

A FAMILY WHO SAT IN FRONT OF US IN CHURCH

rather aloof people, I felt shy to speak first. You know how you always hope the other person will break the ice and speak first, and how the other person hopes you'll do it, so no one does it, and the ice gets firmer and firmer.

One Saturday evening, however, I met the mother out doing her Saturday shopping, and taking courage for my comrade I asked was she well, as I had been missing her. Dear, dear, why hadn't I spoken before? The poor woman was just dying for someone to speak to her. She was quite pleased (as we all are) to find we had been missing her, and then she confided to me the reason of their absence. The son, Tom was his name, had taken his Sunday suit for weekdays, as his working clothes had grown very shabby. He was laying aside every Saturday as much as he could spare to buy himself a new suit, and then she added, with a pleased little laugh, " The boys want to give me a new coat, the same as the one you wear on Sundays."

Well, well, how much we miss by not being friendly with each other. How proud I was to tell her that my son Jack had sent me my Sunday coat out of his first earnings, and if you choose to think I'd change it for one of Queen Mary's, why, you're quite wrong. Then and there we had a talk about our sons, and we parted like old friends and promised to go and see each other.

Sunday " a day different "; yes. " Oh day, most calm, most bright, the week were dull, but for thy light."

MEMORIES

THERE was never such a time as the present for collecting. Children collect postage stamps, cigarette pictures, tram-car tickets, buttons and birds' eggs. I know one little girl who is collecting all the recipes given away with a certain brand of baking powder. Another young friend collects the silver paper which is used to wrap up chocolates and chocolate biscuits. She tells me she sends boxes of this tinfoil to some hospital where it is used to make limbs for the limbless.

Grown-ups collect old china, rare books, furniture,

pictures, jewels and all manner of things. I once knew a man whose house was like a museum with old treasures and he hadn't a moment's peace of mind. He was always afraid of fires or floods or burglars or accidents of some kind or other.

Well, there is one form of collecting we can all do. It costs us no money and it needs no time. It will enrich our lives and no burglar or highwayman can steal it, no careless person can break it, no fire or flood can destroy it. It is ours for ever. Unlike other collections it will add to our happiness but not to our anxieties, and though we give part of it away we still have the whole to ourselves.

A puzzle, you say? No, not much of a puzzle. I'm speaking about collecting memories. We should all collect them—happy ones chiefly—and we'd be amazed at how big a collection we have.

An old blind friend of mine—one of the most contented women I have ever known—told me that she had such a collection. In the days of her youth she had stored her mind with beautiful verses and poems. " I just go over old favourites," she said, " and I am so thankful my mother and my teachers made me commit to memory so many beautiful pieces of writing. I didn't know then that the day would come when my eyes would fail me. I have them all now stored in my memory and no one can take them from me."

It's strange, too, how little poems we learned as children at school have stayed in our memories all these years. They are often much fresher than things we heard only last week.

Don't you remember how we used to weep about poor Lucy Gray, the solitary child?

> "No friend, no playmate Lucy had,
> She dwelt on a wild moor.
> The sweetest thing that ever grew,
> Beside a cottage door."

Lucy became a friend of ours—we expected to meet her at any street corner, and even yet to go over the verses is to collect again memories of our childhood.

The girl who lived next door to us had to commit to memory a perfectly horrid poem called " Little Jim." It was a dismal tale and poor Maggie Mitchell could hardly keep the tears out of her eyes when she began:

> "The cottage was a thatched one,
> The outside old and mean,
> Yet everything within that cot
> Was wondrous neat and clean."

The poem goes on at great length to describe the death-bed of little Jim. I came across a reference to the poem the other day and, like a flood, old memories swept over me—things I thought I had quite forgotten.

Sometimes a whiff of perfume sets us collecting old memories. An old chum of mine once told me that the smell of honeysuckle always awakened in her mind

THE SMELL OF HONEYSUCKLE WOULD DRIFT
INTO THE ROOM

a feeling of home-sickness. She said, " When I was a small child I had a long illness and when I was getting better I was sent to stay with my Aunt Bessie. She had a cosy, little, whitewashed cottage and round my bedroom window climbed the honeysuckle. I used to be sent to bed in the daylight and sleepless and wide-awake

I used to lie in bed. It was then the smell of the honey-suckle would drift into the room and the smell always made me home-sick. To this day the smell of honey-suckle fills me with memories of sadness and home-sickness and I see again that lonely little girl who wanted her mother and father and brothers and sisters, oh, so badly."

A strain of music or an old song are other memory bringers. When we are out collecting we get many memories from this source. Looking back at the past, it was simple little childish songs we loved best. We can remember the first time we heard someone singing "Auld Robin Gray" or "Annie Laurie." To hear these melodies is to recapture our youth. Memories of old companions whose very names we had almost forgotten come crowding back and we say, " Why, I'd almost forgotten that old friend." Because the memory brought back the name, crowds of other memories come too. And so our collection grows.

Just now when people are getting the rubbish in their gardens all gathered up, when furze and last year's heather are being set on fire, the air is full of the smell of greenwood. There is nothing in all the world like this smell for helping the collector of memories. In a flash we see again old roads along which our feet used to travel when we were young—we see the hillside and the happy young folks setting the bushes on fire. We see the frosty red light in the western sky and memory with all her busy train brings us hosts of treasures for our collection.

GROOVES

Do We Like Them?

I wonder if we women aren't to a great extent prone to let our lives get into grooves—especially we older women? In the little everyday affairs of life we are quite content to go on in the same old groove from one year's end to the other. How often we say, " I don't hold with this new-fashioned way of doing things! " and we say it quite proudly. We should be ashamed to say it, for the way of the groove is the way of the grave. We grow old before our time, simply because we have let our lives get into a groove.

I'm speaking out of my own personal experience now. When John, full of delight, bought me one of these new-fashioned mops, I viewed it with suspicion. I read the directions—and sniffed! " If it does all the advertisement says it can do, it's not a mop, it's a housemaid and an angel all rolled into one," I said to myself, for I wouldn't have said it aloud to hurt John's feelings for all the world. All the same, I had my doubts about it.

Well, I poked it beneath beds—beneath the dresser—beneath the mangle—beneath everything that was hard to dust under, and it came out every time full of dust and fluff. "A vigorous shake outside is enough to remove the dust," said the book of directions. I accordingly took my mop to the door, and I must say it gave me a great surprise to see how much dust came out of it when I gave it a " vigorous shake."

Still I didn't believe the floors were properly clean. No, no, I must needs get down on my hands and knees, and poke and push a duster beneath the furniture. The duster came out quite clean; the mop had really fulfilled its promise. So deep in the grooves of old-fashioned ways was I that I tried a second time, with the same result. Then it dawned on me that I was in a groove—a sure sign I was growing old.

It was at this time I got the loan of a very amusing book. It described the adventures of an old Scotch woman in Italy. She was a sort of confidential maid to two young ladies who were travelling about from place to place. Old Margaret had never been out of Scotland before, and was waist deep in the groove of old-fashioned ways. She used to write the most amusing letters to her old friends in Scotland, and in everyone of them she reported how the servants in Italy did their work. They always did it differently from her, and she therefore concluded they were all wrong! For instance, she saw them dusting and polishing floors without once going down on their hands and knees. They took different kinds of long-handled brushes and mops— even the shovel had a long handle, so that they had

I MUST NEEDS GET DOWN ON MY HANDS AND KNEES

not to stoop. What laziness! The old Scotch woman was boiling with indignation. She wanted to take these Italian maids to Scotland, to see how we Scotties go down on all fours and use quantities of elbow grease. All the same, she couldn't deny that the floors looked as clean as if they had been polished by hand.

The pavements were cleaned by having water sluiced

over them, and then brushed with a hard-bristled broom. She condemned this straight off! But the pavements dried quickly; there was no doubt they were perfectly clean; and instead of aching knees and back and red swollen hands, there was only a wet broom, set head upwards to dry, and an empty bucket, to show that the work was done. The maid was dry, and untired. Grooves! Why there isn't a woman of us who isn't deep in them.

We think when we read advertisements about electric vacuum cleaners that we'd love to have one. Would we? The price is prohibitive, and we sigh, and give our husbands to understand that we are rather ill-used because we haven't got these aids to housekeeping. Is there a woman of us who would really believe that our beds and mattresses were properly cleaned by a vacuum? Not a bit of us! We'd never be satisfied till we'd lugged all our beds out into the fresh air, and pommelled them well with a carpet cane.

Mrs. Allen's daughter, who is a cook in London, sent her mother all sorts of labour-saving things, including a hay box. It was quite a pretty-looking box, with a cushion on the top. Mrs. Allen used it as a seat, but never once as a stove. Then one day she thought she'd experiment. She was going to church, so she put her dinner into the box. To her surprise, when she got home she found the food not only hot, but cooked, and ready to eat. She's out of her groove now, and is preaching the gospel of the hay box to us all.

My sister-in-law, who came from Canada, marvelled when she saw me standing to do my ironing. " Why don't you sit? " she said. " You're spending your strength needlessly."

Mercy on us all—I didn't believe I could get the right polish on John's collars, if I didn't stand—yes, bend—over the ironing table.

" Get a high chair," said my sister-in-law. " We all have them in Vancouver, and we sit and do most of our work. It's silly to stand when you can sit."

Yes, I know our grannies and our mothers all stood when they worked, and we've got into the same old groove, without bothering to think for ourselves.

If any man is reading my chat, and is laughing at women for being in a groove, let me ask him is he one inch better? Didn't he regard with liveliest suspicion the first safety razor? His father had used an old-fashioned one; he'd go on using one the same. When he got a " safety " as a Christmas present he had it for ages before he tried it. Then he tried it in a gingerly fashion, and behold, it did its work all right. So now he is out of that groove.

I am preaching the gospel of get-out-of-your-groove to myself as well as to my readers. It's awfully good for us.

DON'T GET BURIED TILL YOU'RE DEAD

I was reading the other day the life story of a brave and gallant man. His had been a hard life, a fight from the very beginning. He had got on but it had been by sheer perseverance. Then when things were getting easier his wife, who had been his comrade, died. His children were all married and in homes of their own. He was utterly lonely, and rheumatism, which had been worrying him now and again, came and made its home in his hands and feet. He had no will to fight. Day after day he used to sit in an armchair by the fire and it seemed to him that death was the only thing he had to look forward to. He was allowing himself to get buried before he was dead. He gave up one by one his places on committees and councils. He ceased to have much interest in the topics of the day. His hands were so painful he could not write and so he got out of touch with his friends and he was daily dying inch by inch. His life was over.

Then one day the sun shone and he hobbled from the fireside to the window and sat down in the light. The warmth of the sun seemed to get into his bones; it did more, it spoke to his heart and he felt his spirits rising. This is what it said: " Why don't you try the new cure the doctor told you about? Give it a chance. Don't sit still any longer and let your joints grow so stiff that they won't bend. Try exercise. Come out into the sunshine. Try to write to your friends once more—don't lose them for want of writing to them although it would only be a short letter. Why do you not read the newspaper and take an interest in what's going on in the world? Make up your mind you're going to get better and take up your golf again. *Don't get buried till you're dead.*" It was not easy, but something told him that by putting off it would only be more difficult. One by one he got into touch with his old interests, and life was good and full and happy.

Isn't it a fine, cheery slogan for us who are no longer young? If we begin to pity ourselves and to say life is over we're done for. Up, up, then! let's shake ourselves as in the days of old. There's heaps of things for us to do. We may have rheumatism in our feet so that we can't walk but we needn't have rheumatism in our minds; we can see that there are crowds of people far worse off than we are.

A very distinguished lady was lecturing the other day to a large audience and she took for her subject " Marriage." She said some wise words on this important subject, and she gave her hearers some excellent advice. " Laugh a bit, chaff a bit, put a spice of humour into the matrimonial mixture," she said. If you " laugh a bit " believe me you'll have no time to pity yourself, you'll be so busy laughing at yourself and your life will be all the healthier for the laughter. You'll certainly have no time to think of the churchyard and to tell everyone that your life is over.

Miss Kerr of the Crofts took cataract on her left eye. The doctor advised an operation but Miss Kerr wouldn't hear of it. " I'm old," she said (she was sixty), " and for all the time I'm likely to be left in this world I'll just do with my right eye." So far as money was concerned she was well-off, but she had no relations nearer than Australia and so she was left alone. She just folded her hands and agreed that she was as good as dead. She gave elaborate directions for her funeral and lived a life of gloom.

Then one day her grand-niece Jenny came home from Melbourne. She was a bright, gay colonial girl full of " pep," and her great-aunt's funereal ways drove her crazy. How she managed it no one ever knew, but Miss Kerr went to a good nursing home and the operation was successfully performed. Home she came again as good as new—far better than she had ever been, for Jenny had insisted upon her getting a stock of new clothes. When the old lady had suggested that a shroud was all she needed, Jenny all but shook her and never rested till she had bought herself a new fur coat! She made her get new hats too, and I suppose the battle they had over the length of the new skirts was furious—but Jenny won the day!

Now instead of heading her course for the churchyard, what do you think has happened? She has gone for a trip to Australia with Jenny! She's to spend a year at least visiting her relations and when she returns she's to start a poultry farm and later on she may go in for bee-keeping. She's evidently made her mind up that she is not to be buried till she's " good and dead."

Well, we can't all afford to go for trips to Australia, but there are other pleasures well within our reach. Get out into the sunshine and let God's good gift work its magic on you. I am always thankful that char-a-bancs are so plentiful and so cheap now. We can for a few shillings see more of our lovely land than our forefathers could ever manage to do. Don't go to the churchyard till you've seen how wonderful this old world of ours is. Too old? Not a bit of it. Did you see in the papers the other day the picture of a young lady of sixty-seven who was learning to ride a bicycle? I have called her a young lady and so she is. Her years may number sixty-odd but her heart is not a minute

A YOUNG LADY OF SIXTY-SEVEN

older than seventeen. She explained that she had wanted all her days to be able to cycle and she had to wait for years to attain her object. Most of us would have said at her age, " Never mind. There's no use bothering now. Soon I'll be in my grave." Wasn't she a plucky old sport? I expect that before she's done with life she'll be flying to Paris; probably she'll act as her own pilot too!

And after all this fine talk I must get up and get out. Jack wants me to learn golf and I have had to listen to a lecture from my son. I said I was too old. Guess what he said. " Why don't you practise what you preach? "

ANGELS

" I don't believe in angels," said a young woman to
her mother one day. " Don't you? " asked her mother;
" yet there were two of them in this street last night.
A little child was born in No. 5, and in No. 19 an old
man died. The angel of life came with the child; the
angel of death took away the old man."

It's a pretty story, but with all due respect to it I'd
like to add another angel, one we can see and talk and

listen to, one who generally comes along with the angels of life and death. She doesn't look like a conventional angel with wings and a halo. She wears a neat navy blue coat and a smart little cap, and when she takes off her coat and hangs it on a peg behind the door and says, " Now then, let me have a look at you," why, we just heave a sigh of relief and say, " The angel is come—it's all right." We call her " Nurse "—our district nurse. Her presence cheers us, and her kind clever hands make us feel in another world as she arranges pillows, straightens bedclothes and conjures up tidiness from confusion. I wonder what life would be like for us working women without the district nurse, this angel in blue upon whom we all rely in our dark hours? When people tell me the world is going steadily from bad to worse I ask them to consider our hospitals, to consider our nurses and then to tell if a world with so much good in it is going to the dogs? The answer is in the negative, as politicians say.

Our nurse has always been a welcome visitor ever since that black winter when John took pneumonia, and the boys very thoughtfully took 'flu at the same time. It was a terrible winter, but thank God we pulled them through, and how much was due to nurse and her unceasing care I shall never forget.

She came in the other afternoon, not to visit me, but to beg, as she said with a laugh. " You'll sit still until

I make you a cup of tea," I cried. "You look as if you'd been up all night."

She did not deny it. "A baby case," she said, " and after everything was well over I was called to a case of burning in Kirk Lane." Then she went on to tell me how an old woman had upset a paraffin lamp. The flames caught in her skirt and her legs and hands were badly burnt. " Have you any old linen for bandages? " she asked, and I said, just for the pleasure of keeping her a little longer, that I'd go and see when she'd finished her tea.

It's wonderful what even a quarter of an hour's rest and a cup of tea will do to revive a tired woman. By the end of that time nurse was looking ever so much better. She had recaptured her sense of humour, too, a sure sign that she was getting over her tiredness. " Do you know that old woman in South Street? " she asked, " the one who wears so many shawls." I said I did. " She has a bad cold and she can't understand how she caught it, because she solemnly told me she hadn't washed her face for three weeks, nor taken off her shawls day or night." Nurse finished her tea, and armed with a roll of old linen took her departure.

She used to pass our door every morning to this burning case, and sometimes I used to coax her to come in and rest. The patient, old Granny Dow, was rather a difficult person. She had a rooted antipathy to being washed. Why she should be washed every day was a mystery to her. One day she said, "Are you married, nurse?"

"No," replied nurse, going on briskly with her work.

"ARE YOU MARRIED, NURSE?"

"If I were married I wouldn't be able to come here every day and wash you."

"It's a pity," sighed old Granny, "a *great* pity...." Then after musing over the case for a little while she added, "You're not married, but maybe when you get over the *disgrace* of being single you're as well as you are."

She felt she'd said something handsome, and could not understand why nurse laughed so much. To her it was no laughing matter.

She went on to give nurse her views on the subject of marriage. She had married at nineteen. " He was only a mill hand, and maybe too fond of a glass, but at any rate he married me. And when my daughter Meg married at the same age I said to her, ' I'm glad, Meg, you're getting married. A woman without a husband has an *awful bare look*'."

" I'm trying to live down the disgrace of being still a single woman," nurse laughed, as she rose to depart.

In these new-fashioned days when marriage versus a career are so carefully pitted against each other, it's refreshing to hear such truths. All the same, it's a jolly good thing for us that our angels down below choose the career.

CONSIDER THE NETTLE

I**f** the enthusiastic promoters of flower shows were to offer an award for the biggest nettle grown in the smallest garden, I'm quite sure we'd get first prize!

Not only are our nettles big in size, but their stings are simply *fierce*. I am speaking with great feeling, having just come in from the garden where I was gathering some late blooms. Frost had just begun to nip the pretty edges of the dahlias and chrysanthemums, but no frost ever affects the nettles! In fact, I think they thrive on frost and flourish in sleet.

I had to step in the most gingerly fashion round the plots in order to avoid the nettles and to get the chrysanthemums; but even so I got stung all over my hands and wrists. I showed my swollen hands to my husband in order to reproach him for not doing his weeding better and also to get a little much-needed sympathy.

I managed neither!

132

Reproaches? He calmly told me that I'd only myself to blame for going into the garden. Sympathy? He said, "Grip the nettle good and hard and it won't sting you. In the meantime, dab on iodine."

All very fine, but few of us have the fortitude to grip the nettle "like a man of mettle," and the horrid weed, as if it knew we were cowards, stings us viciously.

Determined to be brave, I made another attempt at getting the last of the flowers. A nettle, a cocky, tall plant, bristling with wickedness and venom, said, "You shan't touch me, nor the flower I'm guarding. If you do, I'll sting you."

I put on as brave an air as I could and I said, screwing up my courage to the sticking-point, "But I shall touch it and you too. There!"

I shut my eyes tight and grabbed. In the bottom of my heart I didn't really believe I'd get the better of that impudent nettle. Well, I'm proud to say . . . I did!

I grabbed it with such fierce determination that the whole caboodle came up by the roots! With the air of a conqueror I flung the noisome weed into the ash-bin, and with my bare, unstung hands I attacked a second with the same happy result. There was a delightful feeling of satisfaction in rooting out these nettles, and also in conquering my fear of them.

Sometimes, when we're facing the day's work, we ask God to send us an easy day. We hope we won't have very heavy burdens to carry. We pray that life may be kind to us and our burdens light.

It's a coward's wish. It's what I was doing when I went to work among the nettles, walking delicately and hoping I wouldn't be stung. But I was stung, and badly too! A far braver thing is to grip the nettle and choke the poison out of it.

I have a tear-off calender with a motto for each day, and to-day's is very suitable for a cowardly creature like me who wants to walk softly instead of bravely. This is it:

" Don't ask for easy burdens, ask for strength to carry heavy ones."

And after all this brave and courageous talk I'm wondering how I'm to screw up my courage to tell the baker that the last loaf I got from him was so dirty we couldn't eat it, and that I'm afraid I must go elsewhere for my bread.

Our old baker has retired and this is a new one just beginning to work up a connection. I'd like, for the sake of his wife and children, to give the man a chance to " make good." At the same time, I can't afford to buy bread which is unfit for eating.

" Grip the nettle," I said to myself. Yes, yes, I know, but goodness me—isn't it hard to do? I hate having words with people.

" Be brave," I said to myself when I heard the baker's

whistle at the door. I was trying hard to remember that it doesn't pay to be cowardly. It's bad for one's own

"I'D LIKE TO TELL YOU HOW GRATEFUL I AM"

character to shirk a duty because it's disagreeable. Thus did I speak to myself. I also said, "Your backbone will become your wishbone if you're so cowardly."

So I grabbed my purse and basket and with a face of

grim determination I sallied forth. I'd a nice little speech all ready in my head to fire off. I meant to point out to the man his mistake.

" Good morning," I began pleasantly, saying to myself all the time, " Remember the nettle."

That was all the length I got. " Oh, Mrs. Mackay," he said in a most contrite tone of voice, " I think it's awfully good of you to come for another loaf after the last one I sold you. We were cleaning the oven, and I don't know what happened, but pieces of coke and lumps of soot and lime got into the batch of dough and spoiled the whole lot. I have had dozens of complaints —you are the only one who hasn't said a word about it. I'd like to tell you how grateful I am."

I hadn't to grab my nettle after all! All my brave talk and screwing up of my courage was in vain.

" I was going to speak about it to-day," I said, " if you hadn't begun first." And then we both laughed.

Quite a lot of our troubles are like that; once we've firmly made up our minds to *grab* them, behold the need to do so has vanished. All the same, the making up of our minds is good moral exercise.

BLACK MAGIC

WE always read with interest about crystal gazers and marvel at their powers of telling the future. Well, after all, it doesn't do much good to know the future—now does it? And if we want to work a spell we can do it ourselves quite well. We don't need a crystal ball, a black velvet cushion and the dim light! Not at all. A penny bottle of black ink will work much more effectively, and if carefully used will bring a lot more pleasure and real happiness to our friends than any vague prophecy of the future which the crystal gazer may utter.

The black magic which we can all perform isn't the horrid sinister thing we associate with the words. For the working of this spell you need—ink—a sheet or two of notepaper (and goodness knows we don't need to lack that so long as itinerant merchants persist in selling us writing pads)—a pen—not a fountain one. I never knew a fountain pen that could do anything but drop inky tears and splutter badly. Get a good nib in a nice wooden penholder, and there you are. You can begin weaving your spell with such simple materials as these. Some careful spell-weavers like to have a dictionary handy. But it's not really necessary; in fact it often cramps your style.

You remember the old lady who, when she wasn't sure how to spell a word, underlined it. If it were properly spelt her friends thought she wished to add emphasis; if it were wrong then the underlining was meant for a joke. She was safe whatever happened. So don't bother about the dictionary.

We read in old tales of knights who, when they got their first sword, used to lay it on the altar and spend the night in dedicating themselves and their sword to redressing all wrong. It wouldn't be a bad thing if we did the same with our pens. I don't mean that we need go and spend a night in some church, but it's not a bad thing, when you're in bed, to plan just what you will say when you're writing to your friends.

You wish to get into touch with some distant friend and only the black magic of pen and ink can do this for you. Christmas and New Year times give us a golden opportunity for getting into touch with those neglected but still loved friends. And there's no blinking the fact that as we grow older our friends are fewer and fewer. Let us then " grapple with hooks of steel " to our souls our old friends.

In weaving your spell (you can if you like call it " writing a letter ") don't waste time with apologies; just tell your friend how you've been thinking about her. At this time of the year reunions mean so much to us all, and if we cannot meet in person we can meet in letters. Recall to her, too, some happy experience you have shared with her; tell her your last joke, and don't forget to ask about her favourite hobby, which may not appeal to you but is beloved by her. (I once had a friend who kept a tortoise and she'd speak about it for hours. You never can tell how even your nearest and dearest will act!) Put kind feelings and loving thoughts into your letter, for the writing " between the lines " is the real spell, and before you've time to change your mind hurry off to the nearest pillar box and commit your spell to the postman. He and the railway train will do the rest.

When your friend reads your letter, laughs at your joke, and recalls your mutual experiences and likes you, too, for remembering her hobby—why she's quite forgotten to be angry with you for not replying to her last letter (dated last May), and the chances are she'll sit down and write you a letter that will warm the cockles of your heart. Now, could gazing into a crystal ball perform half such a wonderful spell or bring such delightful results as dipping a pen into an ink bottle?

" THIS LETTER TELLS ME THERE WERE
TWO LOAVES SENT "

A letter always seems such a living thing; there is so much of the writer in it that it says far more than the actual written word.

Last Sunday we had a missionary from Africa telling us about his work there. To begin with the black boys regarded books and writing of all kinds as magical. One day the missionary wrote a note and gave it to one of his boys to carry to another mission station and bring back the reply. The letter asked for the loan of one loaf.

The black boy got the loaf, in fact he got two loaves and a note from the second missionary telling his friend he was sending two loaves in case one would not be enough. The bread was newly baked; it smelled deliciously. Sambo could not resist the temptation; he sat down on a handy stone and ate a whole loaf.

Beaming with honest endeavour he reached his home and handed one loaf to his master and the note. When the missionary read it and saw only one loaf he said, " This letter tells me there were two loaves sent— where is the second? " Sambo, the picture of injured innocence, said, " How did the letter know? He didn't see me! I sat on him all the while I was eating that loaf."

I'll tell you another excellent use for black magic. If you're angry with someone, seize your pen and write down all the reproach and anger that's in your heart and then post the whole thing—*in the fire*. You'll feel ever so much better, and no one's a pennyworth the worse for your getting this off your chest.

TAKING IT "ON THE RUN"

WE get an amazing amount of fun out of things by taking them "on the run." I've often noticed that a carefully planned day, every moment of which has been scheduled, often turns out a dreary disappointment. Some other day when we take things "on the run" has turned out a great success. Often the day upon which we'd planned to go for a picnic turns out either wet or windy, and all our careful arrangements are useless. Then some other day because the sun is shining we suddenly decide to have a picnic, and it's a great success though it's done "on the run." True, we may not have all the "posh" things of our first picnic, but we've got the sun shining. Let's take things "on the run." Why, the very sands run; a ladder in your stocking runs; our clocks run; let's run too!

The fun one gets out of this is wonderfully refreshing. It keeps our hearts young, and makes our eyes quick to see the things worth seeing, and it leaves behind it a store of happy memories.

Last October, Captain Breezy went out to post a letter. There is a pillar box at the corner of his street. It was late and his wife was in bed, but he thought he'd just slip along and post his letter. It was a lovely moonlight night with a gay little breeze. The Captain dropped his letter into the pillar box, and then he thought he'd go a little bit further. He remembered, however, that he did not close the street door. Never mind! he'd be back in a twink, and all his neighbours were honest folks.

He had on ancient carpet slippers, and with his hands in his pockets and an old hat on his head he sauntered along. On and on he strolled, forgetting everything except the fineness of the night. At last he reached Hill Street. All the houses in this street have pretty gardens and in the end house, where Mr. Thomson the tailor lives, there are a number of apple and pear trees.

It was too dark for the Captain to see the gardens, so he was just turning back when a wicked little puff of wind blew his hat right into Mr. Thomson's garden.

Now Mr. Thomson had been much annoyed night after night by uninvited guests stealing his fruit, so he and his wife had concocted a trap for the robbers. They had assembled umpteen empty cans of all sizes and piled them up in a heap. Then they had fastened thin twine between this pile and their best apple tree. If anyone went near the tree, and touched the string, down would fall the " empties " and out would rush the tailor and catch the thieves. Such was the pleasant programme planned by Mr. Thomson.

The Captain, all unconscious of this, climbed carefully over the garden wall. He could see his hat and put out his hand to catch it when with a wicked jump off it flew. The Captain went in hot pursuit and caught it at the foot of the apple tree. And then—there was a deafening clatter and banging of empty tins, and is there in all the world a more nerve-racking sound? " By—jings," said the Captain, and tried to step back, only to find his feet entangled in the twine. He lost one of his carpet slippers, and when he tried to find it he got more deeply entangled and sat down suddenly and *in italics!* All the time the orchestra of empty tins shrieked and howled and jangled and rattled.

" I've got you, my man!" said a fierce voice at his elbow, and the Captain found himself blinking in the light of Mr. Thomson's electric torch. " Come away, we'll see what the policeman has to say. Where are your companions? "

" Just a minute; wait till I get my carpet slipper and my hat." The Captain spoke meekly.

Mr. Thomson flashed his light, and then, seeing his

captive, he broke into roars of laughter. " Captain Breezy, what *are* you doing here? "

The Captain tried to explain his suspicious behaviour,

" I'VE GOT YOU, MY MAN! "

and Mr. Thomson (who is the Captain's tailor) insisted that he should come into the house and have a smoke. There Mrs. Thomson appeared with hot coffee, and the time passed very merrily till a clock announced that it was midnight. Mrs. Thomson gave the Captain a string bag full of apples for a peace offering.

In high good humour, and chuckling to himself, the Captain began "to steer his course for the home harbour." Neither he nor Mrs. Thomson had noticed a hole in the string bag, till a continued bump-bump made him suspicious. To his dismay, he found only one apple left. Back he went to recover them. He must have been grovelling in the road for hours, because the moon had set and the night was dark, so that he did not notice a pool in front of Bill Campbell's house and went splash into it, leaving behind him a slipper! When he reached his own door, the door which he had left open, he found it had "banged to." "This is not real," he told himself, "this is some awful dream."

After repeated efforts he got his wife to hear, and when she opened the door and beheld him hatless, wearing one slipper, and carrying a string bag in which was one small green apple, she gasped out, "Where have you been?" "I wasn't in the Garden of Eden anyway," the Captain chuckled, "though I got this apple from a woman. By jings, I've had some fun to-night, and it's been all ' on the run '."

HOLIDAYS

IF you consult the dictionary as to the meaning of the word " holiday," you will find that to begin with it meant a " holy day," a day set aside for worship. Then by-and-by people began to use the day for their own amusement; they found that one single day was not enough so they took two or three and called them holidays. Thus the old meaning and the old use of the word got quite lost.

When the day was really a " holy day," hard-working folks must have been glad of it—glad of the freedom from their usual work for " a change is as good as a rest." Perhaps, too, they were glad to go back to their job after the exercises of the " holy day," and if that was the case then their holiday had fulfilled its purpose. After all, what's the good of holidays except to send you back to your old job with a new liking for it, to your old home with a new love for it and to the old friends sure that nowhere else are there any friends like them? " East, West, Home is best."

We all of us dream of the holidays we are going to have some day when we are rich or when we have time, or when the children are grown up. The places we are going to see—the things we are going to do— the people we are going to meet are all to be most wonderful in this dream holiday of ours!

Well, I'm not so sure about it now. There is the case of Mr. and Mrs. Cooper which has set me wondering if our dream holidays had not better remain dreams. These two—I mean Tom Cooper and his wife— celebrated their silver wedding. They had had a long struggle bringing up their family and getting them all launched on their life's work. There was neither time nor money for holidays. But this year things were to be different. The family, fine well-doing young folks, had saved up a nice little nest egg for their parents and it was to be all spent on a holiday. Mrs. Cooper was to have the black silk dress and the embroidered coat she had wanted for years. She was also to have a silver teapot and her husband was to have a silver mounted umbrella and they were to go for a holiday!

The parents loved to have the young folks planning for them. How proudly did they say, "Look at what these daft young people have been wasting their money on." But anyone could see they loved the young people for so wasting their money.

Then it came to deciding where they were to go for their holiday. "I have always thought I'd love a holiday away among the hills," said Mr. Cooper. "Perhaps we might get lodgings in some gamekeeper's or shepherd's cottage and go exploring the place. If there was a loch or a river we might do some boating and fishing, and we could wear all our old clothes, and I wouldn't have to shave. I think I'd love such a holiday."

When he said this his wife's face fell. "Oh, Tom," she cried, "I don't think I'd care for such a holiday. You know I'm always sick if I put my foot aboard a boat. And to wear all our old clothes after me getting a new costume would be very hard. I hate climbing hills—I'm too old, I'm too fat. Couldn't we go to Brighton? It's such a cheery place, with a band playing on the pier and picture houses everywhere. I'd just love to sit on a camp chair watching the people bathe and the children playing and listen to the band."

Her husband folded his paper with dreadful deliberation. "If you want Brighton," he said, "you can go alone. To sit and watch mixed bathing isn't my idea of a holiday, let me tell you."

So the argument went on—so did time and they got no "forrarder." These two who had jogged along comfortably for twenty-five years had their first serious quarrel over this holiday.

OFF THEY SET . . . ONE IN HEART AND PURPOSE

Then, just the evening before Mr. Cooper's holiday was due, they got a telegram from their eldest daughter. She was married to a farmer in Cairnside and a little daughter had just been born to her. By some unlucky chance the young mother had caught measles and she wired to ask could her mother come and take charge of the baby.

That settled it. They forgot all about their dream holiday. They forgot they wanted to go to different places. They only remembered that their daughter and her baby needed them and so off they set, both of them one in heart and purpose again. Mr. Cooper said he had to look after the baby while his wife attended to the mother.

The delightful part of it was that they really had the holiday of their lives. The daughter made a quick recovery and the baby was, needless to say, the most remarkable child in the whole world. Her proud granddad said so, and he should know, for he had quite a lot to do with the small girl. The weather was good and Mrs. Cooper wore her new dress to church the day the baby was christened. It was upon that day that Mr. Cooper shaved, but his wife had been so busy that she hadn't noticed.

They came back from their holiday brown and jolly and happy-looking, and the young mother and her baby came too. The last time I was in their house Mr. Cooper was making a boat to sail in the baby's bath, while the granny made with the sponge great waves and billows in the bath. But no one was seasick!

PRINTED BY
LATIMER, TREND AND CO.
PLYMOUTH